12

on

THE MIND OF MAN IN AFRICA

THE
MIND OF MAN
IN AFRICA

by
J C Carothers

Tom Stacey

First published in 1972 by
Tom Stacey Ltd, 28-29 Maiden Lane,
London WC2E 7JP

ISBN 0 85468 215 5

Printed in Great Britain by
The Garden City Press Limited
Letchworth, Hertfordshire SG6 1JS

Contents

Author's Note

Nearly twenty years ago I wrote a monograph entitled *The African Mind in Health and Disease*, which was published by the World Health Organization. So many new data relevant to this subject have accumulated since then that I have been urged to write again on this theme. The present volume is the outcome. Two points must, however, be emphasized at the start. First, the World Health Organization has been in no way responsible for the present publication. Second, this volume, although its general arrangement is similar and although it incorporates data and some passages contained in the monograph, is a new book. Later studies have so enlightened certain fundamental issues that I have been led to reorganize my views throughout.

The book is concerned essentially with the mentality of man indigenous to sub-Saharan Africa, both in regard to those aspects that are seen as ordinary or normal, and those that are seen as strange or disturbed, by the societies in which he lives. It is thus also and inevitably concerned with the parts that may have been played in his mental development by hereditary and by environmental factors. I have therefore attempted to present the reader with all those data in both these fields that, derived from the New World as well as from Africa, seem most relevant to this theme.

On a personal note which has been pertinent to the writing, one supposes that most writers envisage an imaginary reader. In the earlier book my imaginary reader was "myself when younger still"; in other words a medical man with an enquiring mind, but working in the considerable professional isolation which was the rule in the Colonial Service of the earlier decades of this century. That reader is now dead, both for me and in reality; for people nowadays get around much more, attend symposia, and obtain "the literature" more easily. His place, however, has sometimes latterly been taken by a twin-headed prodigy who, with one of his minds, adheres staunchly to the faith that Africans belong to a different and wholly inferior species of man, and with his other mind, holds the equally staunch faith that all human groups are mentally identical. Each of these heads is ever-watchful for passages which might serve to prove that the writer was a "racialist" or an "anti-racialist". I can only hope that this "reader" will remain imaginary, and that the real readers of this book will be people who do not fail to recognize that certain social and educational racial problems exist and who believe, as I, that a constructive approach to these problems can only be based on an unblinkered survey of the facts.

Apart from acknowledging my great indebtedness to the many writers whose works have been recognized or quoted in the text, I wish particularly to thank Dr Henri Aubin, distinguished pioneer of African psychiatry, who undertook the arduous and very thankless task of translating my earlier work into French, and Dr Simon Biesheuvel, eminent authority on African psychology, for supplying me with so many of his valuable publications. I would also like to thank Mr Tom Stacey, himself a profound observer of African life, for inviting me to write this book. My final thanks are due to my wife for the steady support and encouragement without which this work could never have been undertaken or accomplished.

Introduction

Dr John Colin Dixon Carothers lived a considerable part of his life practising general medicine in Kenya before he took up psychiatry and was assigned as specialist psychiatrist in charge of Mathari mental hospital in Nairobi. It was my privilege some years later to follow him in that appointment. Dr Carothers has never given up his interest in Africa and has been back a number of times as a consultant to several African countries since he retired from the Kenya government service. He writes with ease and clarity and with authority about Africa and its inhabitants.

This book may well be compared with *The African mind in health and disease/a study in ethnopsychiatry*, which Dr Carothers published in 1953. *The African mind* was a pioneering landmark in African ethnopsychiatry, and is much quoted by those who write about African medicine. Unfortunately it is now out of print and a "scarce" book. One may say a word here about the word "ethnopsychiatry", used in the subtitle of *The African mind*. Ethnopsychiatry is the term applied to the study and practice of psychological medicine or psychiatry in different racial or cultural groups, or both. The adjective "ethnic" is applied to designate either race or culture or both. No emphasis on race or culture is made when using these words. Originally, the Greek words *ethnikos* and *ethnos* referred to pagan, heathen, or primitive groups alien to the Jewish and later to the Christian faith. eg. in the Septaguint it referred to the Gentile. It had a religious meaning. Later, it was applied to define "nation", which gave it a geographical, administrative or political meaning. It has only in the last 100 years or so been taken over by study disciplines like anthropology, sociology, psychology, and medicine in order to describe racial and cultural qualities, limits and comparisons. The most pure modern use of the root is in the word "ethnology", the science descriptive of different races and cultures, as differentiated from "anthropology" which deals with the science of man as a whole.

The present work by Dr Carothers, in essence affords readers that which *The African mind* provided, but it is largely re-written with additional data and new material. It is particularly interesting and significant to note that many of the recent authorities cited by Dr Carothers in his new book are native African physicians, who are now writing in all branches of medicine including neurology and psychiatry. At the time Dr Carothers wrote his first book, there was, I think, only one African doctor qualified in psychiatry. Now there are quite a number, some of whom have contributed much to the medical literature and to our understanding of the diseases of man in Africa.

In dealing with matters of health and illness, it is customary to think in terms of education, services and research. To understand the intricacies of ethnopsychology and ethnopsychiatry, it is most important to promote the further study of it by education at all levels, particularly in the primitive and developing countries, in medical schools to give all doctors a groundwork understanding and also in schools of nursing, public health and all other institutions for the training of health and medical care personnel. Even in the highly technologized, advanced, or "developed" Euro-American countries this is not always well done, but in the so-called developing countries, particularly of Africa and Asia, we know that this is often not the case. Similarly, in the service area, the medical manpower (and woman-power) and hospital and clinic facilities for the care of the mentally ill is inadequate in many places, but particularly in the developing countries, several of which do not yet have any mental hospital. Clinical psychiatry is much the same around the world, taking account of the different secondary symptomatologies of psychiatric disorders based on the impacts of the local culture—customs, religions, languages, etc. Also, it seems likely that the incidence of mental disorders is much the same in all countries. Differences are apparent rather than real, and universal figures depend on casefinding and diagnosis. There is still controversy about psychiatric terminology in various places. Standardization of nosology and classification is on-going research at the international level. Psychiatric illness is very much more abstruse than physical illness since there are so few reliable objective indicators other than signs and symptoms.

Research in ethnopsychiatry is much the same as research in psychiatry as generally understood. There is one specific and exceedingly difficult problem, however, and that is the possibility of race difference in the causes and natural histories of illness. There is so much misunderstanding and prejudice about race, thanks largely to politics and propaganda, that it is difficult if not impossible for scientists to deal fully with the matter. In fact, research in neuroanatomy, neuropathology, neurochemistry and psychology relating to different races (of which the African is but one), has almost ground to a standstill in recent years. Most basic scientists and clinicians interested in the broad area of race variations have avoided expression of hypothesis, theory and experiment because of the risks of being misinterpreted. Psychiatry, by its very nature, deals more with racial and cultural variations than other branches of medicine. This concern takes it into highly controversial and complicated aspects of living that other medical specialities rarely touch upon. Dr Carothers has shown objectivity, freedom from emotionalism and much courage in writing of race and culture differences.

Apart from the chance variables of disease, disablement and infirmity, it remains for the determinants of genetics, race and culture to guide the destinies of man. Dr Carothers has attempted, and with considerable success, to integrate these determinants and variables so far as they concern man in Africa.

EDWARD LAMBERT MARGETTS M.D.
Professor of Psychiatry and Lecturer in
the History of Medicine,
The University of British Columbia,
Vancouver, Canada

PART ONE

THE BACKGROUND

Physical Anthropology

This chapter is concerned with the anthropological background of man in Africa, and since no discussion of this can proceed without consideration of the whole concept of race, the first part will deal with this. Thereafter, consideration will be given, first to the archaeological evidence and, second, to the present-day distribution of the several ethnic groups in Africa, mainly with a view to defining the affinities of modern Africans and the field of further study.

The concept of race

Since Linnaean times, the whole world of living things has been classified into species. Although these species, with their binomial titles, are the bricks on to which systematic biology has been built from that time onwards, it remains, as Huxley[133] has stressed, quite difficult if not impossible to give a wholly satisfactory definition of a species. Nevertheless, the definition that Huxley regards as being generally the most satisfactory is as follows:

> "In most cases a species can (thus) be regarded as a geographically definable group, whose members actually interbreed or are potentially capable of interbreeding in nature, which normally in nature does not interbreed freely or with full fertility with related groups, and is distinguished from them by constant morphological differences."

It has often happened for an animal species to spread so widely in the world that those members of its population that live at one end of its range have become totally separated for breeding purposes from those at the other end. In these circumstances the two populations are likely gradually to diverge for the better adaptation of each to geographical, climatic, and other factors that are unlikely to be identical in these separate areas. If this process continues until the two groups of animals become morphologically distinguishable, they are to be regarded as subspecies and given a third name as has happened for instance with the three subspecies of British wrens inhabiting St Kilda, and Shetland, and the rest of the British Isles. To quote Huxley again: "Forms which replace each other geographically and the differences between which do not transcend those between intergrading varieties, are (unless they are proved infertile by experiment) best regarded as subspecies of a large species." If the process has gone so far that they do transcend that limit or they have been proved infertile then the groups will of course have become full species.

To complete this series of definitions it may, and often does, happen that the range of a species is large enough to have ensured that breeding does not occur between its members living at one end of the range with those at the other end, and that this has been so for long enough to have resulted in their having distinctive characteristics; yet at no point is there a geographical barrier to the interbreeding of the population, which thus merges by imperceptible degrees from one terminal extreme to the other. This sort of character-gradient is called a "cline".

To turn to the problem as it concerns human populations one is confronted immediately by the fact that many such populations have been separated from each other both far enough and for long enough to have acquired characteristics that are so strikingly different as to entitle them to subspecific rank, at least in terms of the above definitions. Yet these populations have never remained completely isolated from each other for long; interbreeding has occurred at certain points and edges, and mutual infertility has not arisen.

Clearly therefore man on the earth today is of one species, but his evolutionary position is peculiar. In the case of most animal species that have diverged to the point of developing subspecies, these subspecies continue, as a rule and if they both survive, to diverge until mutual infertility does arise and full specific rank is attained. In the case of man, however, and to quote Huxley: "Crossing appears to have taken place between well-marked subspecies, and the divergent variability is thus due to ordinary gene recombination". Huxley describes this as a recombinational type of reticulate evolution and says, "Man is the only organism to have exploited this method of evolution and variation to an extreme degree, so that a new dominant type in evolution has come to be represented by a single world-wide species instead of showing an adaptive radiation into many intersterile species."

This unique situation can perhaps best be expressed by using the title "race" rather than "subspecies". This will be done in the rest of this book, and it has to be noted that there are certain important implications of this peculiar type of evolution. Dunn[85] puts the matter well when he defines a race in the human context as "a group of related intermarrying individuals, a population, that is, which differs from other populations in the relative commonness of certain hereditary traits". The words "relative commonness" must be stressed, for differences in sizeable human populations are never absolute. Although, for instance, Negro peoples have on the average darker skins than Caucasoid peoples, yet some Negroes can be found with lighter skins than some Caucasoids. Thus, provided the samples have been large enough, there is always a range of variation of each measurable character within each race, and always some overlapping of this range among races; indeed the range of variation for any character is often much greater for the individuals of a race than is the range of inter-racial means. Moreover, evidence obtained in regard to any one character cannot be generalized; each character must be independently assessed; and groupings made solely on the basis of one character are always different from those made on the basis of any other. Nevertheless, where significant mean peculiarities of several characters are shared by a population, some affinity of race may be assumed. On this assumption classifications have been made; and, on the whole, their reality has received support from later evidence, such as that of blood-group distributions.

The physical characters that have been used in such classifications vary in genetic value, for many of these can change on moving to new environments, but within as-yet-undefined gene-determined limits. Thus stature is highly plastic, iris colour is very fixed and most other characters lie between these two extremes.

Human Palaeontology

On the subject of man's pre-history, physical anthropologists fall into schools of thought which are so divergent that it is still impossible to dogmatize about much of it; this is especially true of racial origins both in regard to place and time. In these circumstances it seems best to hear what more than one distinguished anthropologist has to say. This section therefore leans heavily on the works of both C. S. Coon[73, 74] and W. Howells[127]—two writers whose views are sometimes frankly contradictory.

Coon sees man as belonging to five basic geographical races which, prior to the great migrations of the last five centuries, lived as follows: the Caucasoids in Europe, south-west Asia and North Africa; the Mongoloids in East Africa and North and South America; the Australoids in south-east Asia and the Australian archipelago; the Capoids, a title which includes the Bushmen and Hottentot peoples, living in southern Africa; and the Congoids, which includes the Negro and Pygmy peoples, living south of the Sahara and north of the Capoids.

In contrast to the view that all the human races branched off a common stem within the last few tens of thousands of years, Coon[73] believes that "all the evidence available from comparative ethnology, linguistics, and prehistoric archaeology indicates a long separation of the principle races of man". He believes that the genus Homo first emerged, as Homo erectus, about 700,000 years ago, and that its populations in the several Old World continents gradually diverged into subspecies, or races, which evolved in great isolation from each other and in parallel fashion over the next few hundred thousand years. These races crossed the Homo sapiens' threshold at different times, the earliest about 250,000 years and the latest about 35,000 years ago.

Howells would in general agree with this classification of races, but sees the Negrito peoples of southern Asia as being essentially the same race as the Negroes and Pygmies of Africa. As regards their earlier history, however, he believes that Homo sapiens gradually developed on a line of his own and as part of a radiation which also produced the European Neanderthals and Rhodesian man; that this development occurred in Asia, and that after about 35,000 B.C. the other lines disappeared and only Homo sapiens remained, and from then onwards the several races diverged—the Caucasoid remaining the nearest to the original sapiens' stream.

Since the present volume is only concerned with African populations, further discussion of the problem will be confined to the Caucasoid, Capoid, and Congoid races only.

The Caucasoids

Coon[73] believes that, although in Europe from the beginning of the Middle Pleistocene there is a succession of remains which are apparently Caucasoid, it is hardly likely that Europe was the main centre of Caucasoid evolution because the succession is so disorderly there. He finds that the sum of the evidence points to western Asia as being the main region of development of this race during most if not all of the Middle and Upper Pleistocene. In Europe the human remains go to show that men had reached the threshold of the Homo sapiens grade by at least 250,000 B.C. and that from about 30,000 B.C. onwards they were virtually indistinguishable from modern Caucasoids.

These people, whose homelands exhibited climatic extremes from the damp cold of north-west Europe to the dry heat of Arabia, became very diverse physically; more so than any of the other major races. This has led anthropologists in the past to attempt the classification of the Caucasoids into a number of subsidiary races—Nordic, Mediterranean, etc. But these titles only succeed in designating selected individuals of extreme types rather than populations, whereas in fact the populations melt into each other and the whole Caucasoid race is better regarded as a series of clines.

Prior to about 12,000 B.C. these peoples probably made contact with the indigenous African races only at Suez and in southern Arabia but, from then onwards, they entered North Africa in successive waves. They partly mixed with and partly drove southwards the indigenous people to produce the present-day Berber population of North Africa which is still almost fully Caucasoid. However, in the Sudan, the Horn of Africa, and in a belt that runs down the highlands of East Africa Caucasoids shade into Negroes in clines which are no more than 10,000 years old.

Howell's approach differs from this in two major respects. First, he would hold, as indicated earlier, that Homo sapiens only clearly appeared on the scene, with Combe Capelle man, about 35,000 B.C. Second, he believes that a number of skulls, which Coon regards as Congoid and which have been unearthed in East Africa, are really Caucasoid. He says[127] "If skulls mean anything it is the Whites who have been solidly entrenched in East Africa since the later Pleistocene, and anyone else is an interloper"; and if Howells is right in this, it has important implications for the pre-history of the Negro, and especially of the Bushmen, as will be seen.

The Capoids

There are two principal theories of the origin of the Capoids, the first being that they evolved from full-sized ancestors in the southern African country where they lived within historic times; and the second that they evolved, also from full-sized ancestors, but in North Africa, and were driven southwards by invading Caucasoids about 12,000 years ago, and crossed the Sahara by the Tibesti highlands and then followed the East African highlands southwards to their later home in southern Africa. Much later, in historical times, they were driven into the Kalahari. The proponents of both theories thus agree that the Bushmen are descended from full-sized ancestors, that their size reduction began only a few thousand years ago, and that this happened in southern Africa.

Coon strongly favours the second theory on many grounds. Thus, no Bushman-like bones of much antiquity have been found in South Africa; stone tools when found associated with Bushman-like remains show evidence of derivation from a North African stone tool industry of Recent times, and the Bushman rock paintings in southern Africa are not more than a few centuries old.

On the more positive side, several fragments of skulls have been unearthed in Algeria and Morocco of Early Middle to Late Upper Pleistocene age, of which Coon says that they form a single evolutionary (Ternefine to Tangier) line and were certainly not Caucasoid nor especially Negroid, and he believes that these were the ancestors of the Bushmen.

To follow the evidence into post-Pleistocene times, skulls which were Bushmen-like but larger than those of modern Bushmen have been unearthed at Singa in the Sudan, at Homa on Lake Victoria, and at Boskop and Florisbad in the Transvaal, these being probably of early Recent age, or less than 10000 years old. In the northern Transvaal there have been found a number of skeletons of a Capoid population, unreduced in size, who lived there from as late as A.D. 1000 to A.D. 1400. And even at the present time there are pockets of people, in Libya and Tanzania, who show evidence of Capoid influence, either in appearance or language.

Finally, on general evolutionary principles, the geographical boundaries between Bushmen and Negroes in recent times were never an impenetrable barrier, but a clinal region which could never have supplied the isolation required for their separate subspecific evolution; whereas a Capoid origin north of the Sahara could well have done so.

In summary, and to quote Coon again:

"All the evidence that we have received, then, including that of archaeology, of skeletons, and of relict populations, would indicate that the Bushmen, Hottentots, and their larger ancestors are descended from the Ternefine–Tangier line of North Africa; that their ancestors were driven out of that region by an invasion of Caucasoids toward the end of the Pleistocene and during the early post-Pleistocene period; and that they did not begin to undergo a reduction in size until after arriving in their historic homeland, South Africa, South-west Africa, Bechuanaland, and the Rhodesias."

Howells, on the other hand, who does not see evidence of Bushman characters in skulls farther north than those unearthed in the Sudan and Kenya, believes that East Africa was occupied by Caucasoids from the later Pleistocene onwards, and that the Bushmen probably underwent their characteristic evolution (from large- to small-skulled people) in the region from East Africa southwards.

The Congoids

Coon uses this title, for reasons that will emerge later, to embrace the Negroes of Africa in general and the Pygmies of the forests of the Congo and Rwanda. They are dealt with together in this section, since he regards their evolutionary history as being inextricably linked.

It can be said at once that this history is full of uncertainty. In Coon's words[73]: "The origin of the African Negroes, and of the Pygmies, is the greatest unsolved mystery in the field of racial study". He also says: "As far as we know now, the Congoid line started on the same evolutionary level as the Eurasiatic ones in the Early Middle Pleistocene and then stood still for a half million years, after which Negroes and Pygmies appeared as if out of nowhere."

The mystery is due to an almost total lack of fossils of ancient man from the whole of West Africa; a state of affairs which may well continue for some time since bones rapidly decay in acid forest soils.

Coon believes that the earliest men, distinguishable as ancestors of the Congoid race, lived in the savannah lands of West and central Africa from the Early Middle Pleistocene to the Upper Pleistocene; that some of these proto-Negro people were forced by drought to enter the forest belts of western Africa and the Congo where they lived precariously until such time as they became well adapted to forest-living—a process which entails dwarfing—and thus gradually evolved into the Pygmy Congoid race. In his earlier work[73] he suggested that back-crossing then occurred between these Pygmies and the Proto-Negroes of the surrounding savannah to produce Negroes of modern type. In a later work,[74] however, he suggests that they arose from a miscegenation of the Caucasoids who invaded North Africa at the end of the Pleistocene with Pygmies who lived on the northern edge of the forest.

The latter theory seems to supersede the former and to have more evidential support. Coon[74] writes:

"A detailed analysis of 571 modern Negro crania made by advanced mathematical techniques, has shown that these crania gravitate between two poles, a Mediterranean Caucasoid and a Pygmy one . . . the Negroes resemble the Caucasoids closely in a number of genetic traits that are inherited in a simple fashion. Examples of these are fingerprints, types of earwax, and the major blood groups. The Negroes also have some of the same local, predominantly African, blood types as the Pygmies.

"This evidence suggests that the Negroes are not a primary subspecies but rather a product of mixture between invading Caucasoids and Pygmies who lived on the edges of the forest, which at the end of the Pleistocene extended farther north and east than it does now. To this combination may have been added remnant Capoid genes acquired in the Sahara and East Africa . . . We suggest that such a mixture has been going on for at least 15,000 years, or more than 600 generations, ample time for the present regional and local variables to have arisen. We must also remember that Negroes have been numerous only since the introduction of agriculture."

Howells approach would differ from Coon's. Whereas Coon regards the Broken Hill (Rhodesian) fossil skull (which may be about 40,000 years old) as an astonishingly late example of Homo erectus, Howells sees this as a rather late survival of a near-Neanderthal type of man. Whereas Coon sees this skull as showing Negro features and as being possibly ancestral to the negro race, Howells discounts this and believes that, like the later European Neanderthals, it represents the end of a line which disappeared at about the same time or a little later than these.

Howells believes that the Negro homelands at the end of the Pleistocene were the savannahs of the southern Sahara, then much more extensive and better watered than they are now, and that later, with the coming of iron and of yams, they were able to spread southwards into the forest belt. Where they came from initially he leaves an open question since the oldest skeleton which was surely Negro (Asselar man from north of Timbuktu) was probably post-Pleistocene. He says of this: "However, in spite of the poor evidence, we can hardly escape the conclusion that the Negro stock must have existed far back before anything as recent as the Asselar Man. It is too well-defined, too distinctive, to have emerged in a short time span. Changes in body size or form are one thing; the characteristic hair, lips, form of face and ear, all bespeak a racial lineage running back more than a few thousand years." The final Bantu expansion into central, eastern and southern Africa began from eastern Nigeria not before 2000 B.C. and probably rather later.

As regards the African Pygmies, Howells simply sees these as a branch of the Negro stock who were, or became, better adapted to forest life and hunting through their small size; and he makes no suggestion that they played the further part in Negro evolution that is suggested by Coon. The resemblances between the Negro and Caucasoid races, which Coon attributes to a mingling of Pygmy and Caucasoid genes in post-Pleistocene times, would simply be seen by Howells as deriving from the fact that Homo sapiens in a variety of forms spread all over the Old World and that the modern races of man only began to diverge from each other after about 35,000 B.C.

Finally, African populations throughout much of the continent today, especially in the Sudan, the Horn of Africa, and East Africa are a congeries of Caucasoid-Negro clines; and the Bantu of South Africa have surely absorbed many Capoid elements. But all these clines are relatively recent and whether one believes, with Coon, that the former derive from Caucasoid infiltration from the north in recent centuries or, with Howells, that the Caucasoids have been there since the later Pleistocene, would seem to be a minor issue now.

The Indigenous Living Races in Africa

The classification used here follows in general that of Coon, and the population figures are, and can only be, rough approximations.

The Caucasoids

Living as they have done, from Scandinavia to Arabia, and in the great diversity of climates that this implies, the Caucasoids have become much the most physically diverse of all the major races. The skin and head hair colour vary from fair to very dark, and the iris from blue to dark brown. Faces and noses range from narrow and beaked to broad and snubbed, and horizontal facial contours are much less flat than in any other race. The head hair is straight or wavy, greying tends to set in early and balding is frequent. The lips are usually thin and rarely very everted, teeth small to medium and jaws seldom prognathous. The limbs are of moderate length compared with the trunk and the limb muscles long-bellied. Finger-prints show a majority of loops, and eyeball size is medium.

The total Caucasoid population of North Africa is about 55,000,000. There are two major peoples today who are still almost fully Caucasoid—the Berbers, whose ancestors invaded the country from western Asia and perhaps from Europe about 15,000 years ago; and the Arabs, who have infiltrated in successive waves starting over 1,200 years ago. Apart from these there are many Caucasoid-Negro clines in Africa which will come in for more extended discussion under the Congoid heading.

The Capoids

This title includes among living peoples the Bushmen, who show the peculiar characters of this (Capoid) race in their most extreme, and purest, form; the Hottentots who, according to Coon, are a clinal population mostly of Bushman origin but with Negro and perhaps North African Caucasoid elements; and certain relict populations in Tanzania who are closer to Hottentots than to Bushmen.

Their total population is about 126,000 of whom the Bushmen number about 50,000.

(a) The Bushmen

These people are food-gatherers and hunters and now live mostly in the Kalahari Desert of south-west Africa. They are often infantile looking, and are small with a mean stature that varies in the men from about 4' 11" in the south of their range to 5' 2" in the north, the women being 3½" shorter. The cranium is small, and the face very flat, being, by horizontal measurements, the flattest of any race; the eyelids are slitted and often fat-laden (like Eskimos), and the ears are small. The back is straight; the hands and feet small; and the limb muscles long-bellied as in Caucasoids. The skin is yellowish to medium brown and wrinkles deeply in maturity; there is little body hair and the head hair is "peppercorn"—spiralled in tufts with bare scalp intervening. An accumulation of fat in the buttocks, "steatopygy", is common in the women. They show evidence of an adaptation against cold in the vascular anatomy of the limbs, and the blood groups are in general similar to those in Negroes, probably due to the latter having absorbed Bushman genes.

(b)   *The Hottentots*

These people are cattle-breeders. Their present physical appearance suggests, according to Coon, a mixture of Bushman, with Negro. Thus they are a little darker than Bushmen, steatopygy is well-marked, and the mean height of the man is about 5' 4''.

The Congoids

This title includes among living peoples the Pygmies who, as was shown in the previous section, appear in their present form to be the oldest and in many ways the most distinct members of this race and as compared with the other major races; the Negroes who, in many respects, occupy a position between the Pygmies and the Caucasoids; and a number of clinal populations who are the outcome of much later miscegenation. They will be discussed in that order.

Their total population in Africa is about 120,000,000, of whom the Pygmies number about 160,000.

(a)   *The Pygmies*

These people are food-gatherers and hunters and live in the equatorial forest of west central Africa between latitudes 5° north and 5° south, where they are found in scattered groups from the Cameroons in the west to Rwanda and Burundi in the east.

They are exceedingly short with a mean height of *about* 4' 11'' for the men and 4' 8'' for the women, and have relatively short legs especially as to the thighs and long arms especially as to the forearms. They are very loose-jointed and the spine is lordotic.

They are mesocephalic, often with bulbous foreheads and pro-truding eyeballs, and with very broad noses and much pro-nathism. The skin is yellowish to mahogany in colour, the head hair is tightly coiled, and there is plenty of face and body hair.

Mating often occurs between Pygmies and Negroes, but only between Pygmy women and Negro men, so the gene flow is always from the Pygmies. Thus the sickle-cell trait, which these two peoples share, is likely to have derived from the Pygmies.

(b) *The Negroes*

These people in their relatively purest form inhabit the whole of West Africa and, in clinal forms which are often mainly negroid, they occupy most of Africa south of the Sahara.

In regard to their physical characteristics it can be said that, with a few notable exceptions such as height, they stand in all measurable and observable characters between the Pygmies and the North African Caucasoids. Height means vary from 5' 5" in parts of the west coast to 6' 0" among certain Nilotic tribes. The body build is characteristic, with a relatively short trunk and long limbs (especially forearms and lower legs) and large hands and feet, the shoulders are broad, hips narrow, lordosis is marked, the joints are very flexible, and the limb muscles have short bellies and long tendons. The head is dolicho- to meso-cephalic with a protruding occiput and often a bulbous forehead, the eyes are prominent (the eyeballs being about 9 per cent bigger in Negroes than in Whites measured in America), the ears are small and close-set, the jaws protruding with large teeth and everted lips, and the nose is broad with wide nostrils. The skin is glossy black to dark brown, iris black, lips and gums pigmented, the head hair is black and tightly coiled, and the body hair and beard are sparse. There are roughly 7 per cent more sweat glands in American Negroes than in American Whites according to Lewis[161]. The fingerprints show a majority of loops as in Caucasoids.

(c) *The Negro Clines*

Movements of Caucasoid peoples southwards within the last 10,000 years account for the mixture of Caucasoid and Negro characters to be seen today among the peoples of the Nile, the Sudan, the Horn of Africa, and many parts of East Africa. The invaders naturally tended to follow the line of the high plateau which runs from Abyssinia down the Rift-Valley escarpments to southern Africa.

In regard to the Bantu peoples, Coon says: "The last of the north-south movements was that of the Bantu tribes from their home in West Africa across to East Africa and down to South Africa. The living Bantu tribes of South Africa must contain Bushman, and possibly also Caucasoid, as well as Negro genetic elements." It has to be noted also, and as described by Walker,[257], that when the South African Boers, in the course of their dispersion eastwards from the Cape, reached the Great Fish River in 1778 they then for the first time met the Bantu vanguard, the Xhosas, who had only arrived as far south as this a few years before.

* * *

These then are the chief living races of Africa.

This book is not concerned with peoples, European and Asian, who have entered the country in fully historic times. Of the major indigenous races, the Bushmen and Pygmies are now much reduced in number and only likely to survive for long in certain peculiar climatic environments, while the Caucasoids of North Africa are essentially European and West Asian in origin and remain so to this day.

One is thus left with the Negro and with those clinal populations, including the Bantu, who remain essentially Negroid, who number altogether about 120,000,000 people, and who form the vast bulk of the population south of the Sahara. They inhabit an area that corresponds to four of the nine African culture areas described by Herskovitz[124]—the eastern cattle area, the Congo and Guinea Coast and eastern and western Sudans.

With these the rest of this book is mainly concerned, and it has to be noted that these are mainly pastoral—agricultural peoples, and that no attempt is made to deal with purely hunting and fishing people, whose personality development probably follows very different lines.

The African
in the New World

The African is not, of course, today confined to Africa. He has found his way in historic times, usually by no wish of his own, into many parts of the world. In the Old World, apart from Africa, his influence has been slight. In the New World, on the other hand, he has now become a substantial ingredient of the population. This applies to Latin America, to the West Indies, and to the United States and, since his circumstances in all these countries have been different, a few words are required about his history and status in each. For the particulars, the author is especially indebted to the writings of G. Pendle[201] for Latin America; J. H. Parry and P. M. Sherlock[198] for the West Indies; O. Handlin[122] for North America; and M. R. Davie[76] for the New World in general.

Latin America

Within 20 years of the discovery of America in 1492 the Spaniards established settlements in all the larger islands of the Caribbean—Cuba, Hispaniola (now Haiti and the Dominican Republic), Puerto Rico, and Jamaica. Cattle, citrus fruits, bananas, and sugar were quickly and successfully introduced. Since, however, attempts to make the local Indians work were a failure, African slaves were imported into these islands from 1510 onwards. Between 1520 and 1550, in a swift series of astounding campaigns, the Spaniards conquered almost all of what later became Spanish America. Since Spanish interest in the mainland was chiefly with precious metals and the local Indians could be coerced into producing this, Negro slaves played relatively little part in the Spanish countries of the mainland.

The Portuguese landed at the eastern tip of South America in 1500 and laid claim to all the country east of a line 370 leagues west of Cape Verde, or about 46° west longitude. From 1530 onwards, and in a much more leisurely fashion than the

Spaniards, they gradually built and consolidated a vast empire in the country that is now called Brazil. Second only to the local dyewoods, sugar (introduced from Madeira) rapidly became the chief product of this country and, for its large-scale working, African slaves were introduced as in the Spanish West Indies The trade in slaves to Brazil continued till 1853.

In accordance with this brief history, the Negro and Mulatto population of mainland Latin America today is probably about 9,000,000, of whom over three-quarters live in Brazil, though there are also sizeable populations in Colombia and Venezuela.

As regards their status in these countries it is entirely relevant to quote Davie[76] who wrote:

> "The better treatment of slaves in Latin America than elsewhere in the New World had its roots in the custom and law respecting slaves in the Iberian Peninsula, running back to the Justinian Code and supported by church as well as state . . . Under this law slavery was in effect a contractual arrangement between the master and his bondsman. It had nothing to do with colour or race. The church upheld this and maintained that slave and master were equal in the sight of God. The state protected the slave from a harsh master, provided for his marrying, and prescribed the circumstances in which he might be freed. These Iberian laws and customs were carried overseas and governed the relation between master and slave there as in the homeland. Thus the element of human personality was not lost in the transition to slavery from Africa to the Spanish or Portuguese dominions, and this served as a preparation for moral and other responsibilities characteristic of freedom. Abolition of slavery was achieved in Latin America without violence. Today the Negro, south of the Rio Grande, is a respected citizen to whom most doors are open."

Colour as such has accordingly played a relatively small direct part in the recent social life of these countries, class distinctions are mainly based on other factors and there has been little "racial" segregation.

The West Indies

Spanish settlement, entailing the importation of slaves, began in these islands in 1510. English and French settlement of all the smaller islands did not begin until 1624 but thereafter was rapid and culminated in 1655 in the capture of Jamaica from the Spaniards.

The first sugar canes were planted in the English islands in 1637 and in the French islands in 1647. After about 1650 sugar became by far the chief product in all these islands, whereas in the Spanish islands it remained only one product among several. It is of the nature of sugar production that factories on the spot are required, so estates tend to become large, and the small planter is pushed out. It thus also came about that there was no future for indentured labour, no future for the labourer who had looked forward to a place of his own in due course. Yet much labour was required. The need was filled for a time by criminals deported from Europe but, by the same token, there was no place for these when freed. Thus arose the demand for Negro slaves and, whereas until about 1645 the White population had increased to a level of well over 50,000, thereafter it rapidly declined and, by 1700, Africans formed the great majority of the population in most of the British and French islands. The slave trade therefore became indispensable to the sugar industry, for slaves were short-lived and replacement was quicker and cheaper than the rearing of slave children. The trade was a very active and profitable one and remained so throughout the 18th century—the hey-day of the West Indian sugar industry.

The end of this era was at hand, however. In 1791 a great slave revolt in the country later called Haiti resulted within a few years in Negro domination and in the extermination or emigration of all the Whites. In 1808 the British Act for the abolition of the slave trade came into force; in 1833 came the British Emancipation Act; and in 1848 the French Emancipation Act brought a final end to slavery in all but the Spanish islands where it continued till after 1865.

As regards the treatment of the slave in general, perhaps the chief things that need to be said are that the slave, as such, had no rights, that family life was usually non-existent for him, and that the vast discrepancy in numbers between the ruling White and the enslaved African populations can only have engendered great mutual fears and resentments, with the usual hateful consequences. It says much, indeed, for Negro ability to forget wrongs that there is so little embitterment among the islanders today.

The present Negro population of the West Indies is probably over 11,000,000, of whom about half live in Haiti and the Dominican Republic.

The United States

Slavery on a substantial scale came relatively late to mainland North America.

Unlike the West Indies, where land was in short supply and rapidly fell into the hands of a few large land-owners who depended on forced labour, there was plenty of land at first and a large number of independent farmers settled all along the eastern seaboard. Thus, although small numbers of Negro slaves were imported from 1619 onwards, there remained little demand for their services in the mainland colonies until the later years of the 17th century. Then the picture changed. The plantation system was introduced into the mainland colonies where it was applied to the production of rice, indigo, and cotton, and the market in slaves, mostly imported from the west coast of Africa, steadily expanded until the 1730's.

Referring to the plantation system in its fully developed and highly organized form Handlin[122] says:

"The plantation in this form appeared on the mainland towards the end of the 17th century, brought over from the West Indies, where it had already emerged in the cultivation of sugar. The speed of its spread depended upon the appearance of crops to which it could be advantageously applied, the accumulation of capital to finance it, and the development of an adequate supply of slaves. Those conditions were ripe after 1700. There had been no advantages of scale in the cultivation of tobacco; each of the three or four hands on twenty-five acres was as efficient as each of the two hundred on two thousand acres. That was not the case with the tropical crops that took hold in South Carolina and later in Georgia ...

"The worth of the Negro as an investment accounted for the spread of the new form of organization to Virginia and Maryland. Those provinces raised no rice or cotton; and there were no advantages to the large-scale cultivation of tobacco. But they did raise slaves and as long as the surplus could be sold farther south it did not matter if the return from the sales of tobacco were meagre ...

"The plantation system confirmed the divergence in experience between the provinces to the north and those to the south of the

Mason-Dixon line. The owners of the great estates remained a minority of the white population everywhere; in Virginia and Maryland most freemen still tilled their own plots or were served by a handful of Negroes. But slavery dominated the life of the regions in which the plantation took hold."

Following war with England and the achievement of independence, in 1781, slavery disappeared from the northern States, but not from the southern where it was felt that emancipation would lead to a blood-bath (as actually happened in Haiti a decade later). The importation of slaves was made illegal in 1808 and, although some were still introduced illegally from Africa and the West Indies, even until 1862, the numbers were far fewer than in the 18th century.

In spite of this, after 1815 the cotton industry spread remarkably. Thus, whereas at first the chief centres of production had been the States of the south-west from Virginia to Georgia, by 1860 the largest proportion came from the southern belt of States stretching from South Carolina to Texas, and the number of slaves in this belt had risen to at least $4\frac{1}{2}$ million. This situation, combined with the cessation of the overseas slave trade, created a booming market for the surplus slaves of the tobacco- and corn-producing areas in Virginia, Maryland, and Kentucky and a great internal slave trade developed. This development firmly fastened the southern economy to the plantation and to slavery. Southerners could no longer contemplate emancipation, not only because of the fears of the social consequences that had troubled an earlier generation, but now also because it would ruin the whole economy.

The Civil War of 1861 to 1865 was fought ostensibly on the issue of the right of a State to secede but was in its origin closely bound up with the question of slavery. So, when victory came to the North, the slaves throughout the country were emancipated by law. Unfortunately by this time the whole plantation system, with the social segregation by colour this entailed, had become so much a part of the southern way of life that any dramatic change had become unthinkable there. Emancipation in any real sense could not be created by a stroke of the pen, and the southern Negroes' social inferiority remained as firmly established as before.

Emancipation has gradually become more real in the succeeding years, but is still far from complete and highly dependent on

* *

the outcome of the policy of educational desegregation, as this affects the southern States.

The Negro population of the United States was probably 20,000,000 in 1965, but a large proportion of these are far from pure Negro. Miscegenation was common in the days of slavery, and Herskovitz (as quoted by Davie[76]) has calculated that only 22 per cent are pure Negro, the remainder being mixed with White and to a lesser degree with American Indian blood. Inbreeding however, is now occurring among American Negroes and is producing, according to Herskovitz,[125] a "distinctive type that lies about halfway in its physical traits between the characteristics that differentiate its Caucasoid and Negroid ancestry".

The African Environment

Wherever populations exist and hold their own, it must be assumed that some viable equilibrium is achieved among all the hereditary and environmental factors; that all these factors are inter-related in a fashion to make life both livable and worth-while; and that any ill-considered alteration of any single item, no matter now evil it may seem from the standpoint of another culture, is likely to upset that equilibrium.

These remarks apply in the environmental field to geography, climate, infections, nutritions, and culture. These five items will therefore be considered seriatim in this chapter.

Geographical Factors

Jacobs and Stern[134] writing of cultural and technological differences between peoples, say:

"Variations in geography or climate are not adequate explanations. Britain has had the same climate for ten thousand years past but has exhibited great changes in culture. The tremendous achievements of Egyptians and Mesopotamians in pre-Christian millennia contrasted with their way of life in more recent times suggest that factors of a non-geographic kind must have been operative. The differences of cultural achievements in Peru, Mexico, Japan, India, Sumatra, or Nigeria in different centuries indicate that climate and geographical environment cannot have been the dynamic factor responsible for divergent cultural manifestations in successive centuries. Geography and climate made possible important features of these cultures, but clearly did not cause cultural changes."

No doubt geographical and climatic factors are never the whole story. Their influences are usually highly indirect and act mainly through the other factors mentioned. Nevertheless, they cannot be ignored or even regarded as other than fundamental.

Indeed, it is worth while turning, for a moment, to the wider world to see in what sorts of country cultures of an advanced type first emerged into the light of history. One finds, in fact, that the earliest of such cultures in Asia were in the river-valleys of Babylonia, of the Yellow River, and of the Indus; in Africa, in the valley of the Nile; in Europe they were in Crete and later in Greece and its islands; while in the New World they were in Mexico, Guatemala, and Peru. These regions have this in common, they are all areas where agricultural populations could live in some security, due to a high degree of isolation from other populations. This isolation was a geographical one, dependent in Africa and Asia on surrounding deserts and mountains; in the New World on living on high plateaux surrounded by sea or thick forest; and in Europe on living in islands or isthmuses entirely or largely surrounded by sea. It has therefore to be noted that the geographical factors appear to have done far more in all these instances than make "possible important features of these cultures", for they do seem to have provided opportunities without which these advanced and highly-organized cultures could not have arisen in the first place.

To return to Africa; this continent, with an area of 11,700,000 square miles, is the second largest in the world. But, although its area is over five times that of Europe, its coastline is little more than a quarter as long. South of the Sahara it is strikingly devoid of natural harbours and of rivers that are navigable from the sea. Except for the Atlas Mountains in the north-west, the whole continent is occupied by a plateau with only a narrow coastal plain. The mean elevation of the continent is 1,900 feet, the plateau being highest in the south and east, where much of the country is over 3,000 feet above sea-level. Apart from the deserts and semi-deserts of the Sahara, the Horn of Africa, and the Kalahari, and the dense forest of the Congo Basin and the Guinea coast, the rest of the country is mainly grassland or savanna land with scattered trees.

Viewing the geographical features in the context of human social development, it is clear that the Sahara has formed a considerable barrier to the movements of peoples and to the introduction of cultural elements from the north, at least in post-Pleistocene times. Apart from this, and apart from the dense equatorial forest, however, the vast interior of the continent lacks natural barriers to the movements of peoples and offers none of those opportunities for prolonged isolated development that were mentioned above. Highland Kenya, which is comparable in some ways to Peru and might therefore be expected to have become the cradle of an early civilisation, is by no means so inaccessible and stands, indeed, on the very highway of Caucasoid infiltration into southern Africa.

There is, however, an aspect of African geography which, as it seems to the present writer, is of transcendent importance for the development of the mind of man in Africa and which calls for mention at this point.

Whatever uncertainties remain about the racial origins of the Negro, it does seem clear that the ancient homeland of part or the whole of his ancestry was, for several thousand years, the West African forest belt; a belt which was much more extensive in the past than it is at present.

These African forests are something very different from forests of the temperate zone for they are either deep and very dark or, in areas where more light does infiltrate, become a tangled skein of growth. Apart from occasional elephant tracks, rivers, or man-made clearings, they provide few open vistas, and the man who penetrates a few yards into them can easily be lost.

The theme is developed in later chapters that non-literate peoples in general live much more emphatically in a world of sound than do literate peoples, whose operative world is essentially a visual one. But this is particularly true for those non-literate peoples who live in this kind of forest environment, and where, for instance, all strangers—men or beasts or a swarm of bees—are likely to be heard before they are seen.

That the implications of this theme have been of fundamental importance for the mental development of man in Africa will, it is hoped, be made clear in the chapter on psychology, and in the final discussion.

Climatic factors are closely linked with geographical ones and, accordingly, have played an important part in the development of peoples.

Huntington[130] on the basis of studies of the efficiency of working groups in America, concluded:

> "Three conditions of climate are of special importance in their influence on health and energy: (1) temperature; (2) humidity; (3) variability. Taking the White race as a whole, the best temperature is an average of not far from 64°F for day and night together. Averages

as low as 60° or as high as 70° are almost equally favourable . . . . For mental work, however, the optimum appears to occur when the temperature outdoors—not indoors—averages a good deal lower than for physical activity, probably about 40° or 45°."

In regard to his second and third headings, the relative humidity should be quite high except in hot weather, and frequent moderate changes in temperature are also stimulating.

Huntington also developed the theme that most of the earliest civilizations arose in sub-tropical climates but that the centre of civilization gradually, though irregularly, moved towards colder lands during the last 5,000 years. He believed that at first men were unable to cope with the low temperature of northern winters, but that as the level of their civilization rose they learned how to conquer this—by better clothing, food, housing, heating, and agriculture. Thus, while very high temperatures remain as much of a handicap as before, low temperatures became less and less of a handicap, and civilizations tended to move poleward.

Africa, according to Kendrew [142] "is the hottest of the continents in respect of the mean annual, the summer, and the winter temperatures". Over three-quarters of its surface lies within the tropics; much more than in the case of any other continent. The isotherms range for all parts of the country south of the Sahara between about 60° and 90°F, and in this continent alone is the 50° isotherm not seen, at least when corrected to sea-level. Near the Equator there is little variation throughout the year. As one proceeds away from the Equator the seasonal change becomes greater, with maximum heat in July in the north and in January in the south, and with relatively cool spells intervening. A sharp distinction must be made between the coast and the interior; at the former temperatures are more uniform at all times; in the latter there is not only a seasonal change but also a very striking diurnal one, especially in highland areas.

The total annual hours of sunshine vary from over 3,000 in the Sahara and Kalahari areas to less than 1,600 in parts of the forest belt. Thus, rather surprisingly, the least sunny belt is equatorial and the sunniest belts correspond to the tropics of Cancer and Capricorn. Humidity is at all times high in the forest belt and on the east coast and becomes progressively lower as one moves north or south, and with a relatively dry belt running down the eastern highlands. Away from the forest and the coast it also shows wide diurnal variations like the temperature.

The mean annual rainfall varies from below 12" in the Sahara, the Horn of Africa, and the Kalahari to over 80" in parts of the tropical forests; while the savanna and grassland areas have a rainfall between about 20" and 60". The latter may, by European standards, seem highly adequate, but in these areas of Africa evaporation is rapid and the rain falls mainly at certain seasons. Too often these seasons are followed by long periods of relative drought, and too often the rain falls in deluges which rapidly reach the rivers, carrying the good earth with them. Partly for these reasons the soil, in general, is poor, and deficient in calcium and phosphorus.

To summarize the climatic position in relation to the major indigenous races: the Bushmen now live in a country where the winters are cool and the summers extremely hot (the temperatures ranging from below freezing to 104°F in the shade) and where there is little rain and the sunlight is bright and the air very dry; the Pygmies and Negroes of the forest belt live in a country where it is warm all the year round, rising to 86°F by day and falling to 68°F by night, with little sunlight, a heavy and constant rainfall, and air that is saturated with moisture; while the Bantu peoples of the grasslands live in conditions which are in all respects intermediate between these.

It is clear from these data that the optimal conditions described by Huntington seldom obtained in this continent, and never in the Negro homeland of the equatorial rain belt. However, while Huntington's findings are in manifest accord with European experience and are doubtless true for them, it is less certain how far they should be applied to Negroes.

Thus Hofmeyr[126] says: "The Negro with his highly pigmented skin, large number of sweat glands, and respiratory system adapted to a hot climate, is very well adapted to a tropical environment, but easily contracts pulmonary disease in cold countries. His pigmented skin acts as a filter, reducing the amount of exposure to ultra-violet rays which while necessary for healthy bone formation, is dangerous in overdoses." A study mentioned by Coon showed that American Negroes tolerate moist heat better and cold less well than American Whites of the same age and economic background. Surprisingly, this finding has not been confirmed for Whites and Negroes in Africa. For Wyndham, as reported by Bieshuevel[27], has shown that Black and White subjects in the gold mines of South Africa react in much the same way to work under conditions of high temperature; the decline in work performance follows the same course and heat stroke is liable to occur at about the same point on the effective temperature scale.

Adaptation to moist heat, however, can also be cultural. European behaviour in the tropics, in terms of dress, meals, working hours, etc., is often quite inappropriate to the climate; and African "indolence" may often be seen as a tempo of life that is far better suited to the local conditions. This adaptation may even be engrained in the African temperament, but this is a matter which will be discussed in the chapter on psychology.

It has to be noted, finally, that some of the highest Negro cultural achievements of the past—high by any standard for the 14th century A.D. (see Davidson[75])—occurred in those very parts of Africa, such as Benin, where the combination of heat and humidity is at its highest; a fact which strongly suggests that adaptation to this sort of climate, whether it be physiological, cultural, temperamental, or some combination of these, is not lacking.

Infective Factors

Infections play, of course, an important part in European psychiatry. But in Africa they occur with such ubiquity and variety as not only to cause much frank illness (with psychiatric concomitants) but, in chronic forms, also to promote a continuing background of ill health which must increase the liability to mental breakdown from other causes. It is also quite possible that, occurring in children, they may sometimes impede further mental development.

Multiplicity of causation is particularly striking in African hospital practice and has been well expressed by Gelfand[111] when he writes: "Whilst the European medical student is taught, as a rule, not to diagnose more than one disease, he must forget this instruction when he is dealing with a Native"; and elsewhere[113]: "It is not uncommon to see Africans with more than one parasitic infection". Infections of one sort or another are seldom absent in the rural African, sane or insane, so although its psychiatric importance in general is undoubtedly great (accounting for anything from 9 per cent to 30 per cent of new cases in figures available to me), the role it plays in particular cases is often obscure.

In the following short summary only those infections that play an obviously important part in African pyschiatry are discussed.

Syphilis

The incidence of syphilis, both acquired and congenital, varies greatly from one part of Africa to another. It is therefore not surprising that neuro-syphilis varies in a similar way. Thus, whereas in Uganda, Muwazi and Trowell[185] found that it accounted for about 30 per cent of all certified cases of insanity, in Kenya the present writer[50] found that only 4·6 per cent of first admissions to the mental hospital there were due to this.

It is, however, more surprising to find how greatly the incidence sometimes varies in time, a fact which Billington[32] has convincingly demonstrated. He showed that prior to 1952 neuro-syphilis was one of the commonest forms of central nervous disease seen at Mulago Hospital, Uganda, but that by 1958 the picture had already begun to change. He showed that, among 34,859 general hospital admissions studied within the earlier period, neuro-syphilis accounted for 0·3 per cent, whereas among 51,643 such admissions studied within the later period it accounted for only 0·036 per cent. This dramatic decrease was probably due to the wide use of penicillin from 1950 onwards.

As regards the types of neuro-syphilis, all those seen in Europe are well represented with the exception of tabes which is surprisingly rare, though one case was seen by Muwazi and Trowell[185] and one was described by Billington[31]. General paralysis is quite frequent wherever neuro-syphilis is common. Its appearance— clinical, serological, and post-mortem—is typical of this disease as described elsewhere, but a large proportion of the subjects are markedly expansive and demented by the time they first come under psychiatric observation in Africa.

Trypanosomiasis

Although this disease has been largely contained, Garnham[107] sounded a note of warning in 1968 when he said "Trypanosomiasis, both human and animal, has the potential of

the widest dispersion in Africa and, under conditions of disorgani-
sation would present the gravest problem. The stability of the
countries of East Africa shows how in such circumstances the
disease can be kept in check—but the menace is only just around
the corner." It must therefore be given more than passing mention
here.

Trypanosomiasis is by no means universal in Africa but is
limited to the tropics, especially on the western side, and occurs
very locally in eastern and central Africa. It exists in two forms,
Gambian and Rhodesian, and although wherever it occurs it is
variable in its clinical manifestations, it can in general be said that
the Rhodesian is a much more acute and fatal disease than the
Gambian. So true is this that the three stages of trypanosomiasis
commonly described—the febrile and toxaemic, anaemic and
debilitated, and encephalitic stages—are often not seen in the
former as the patient commonly succumbs to inter-current infections before the encephalitic stage is reached.

However, the encephalitic stage, which is the main concern
here, may occur in the Rhodesian form and is the chief and often
very chronic stage seen in the Gambian. Tooth,[245] who has
written a valuable study of this disease as it occurs in the Gold
Coast, states that "it is probably the commonest cause of mental
derangement throughout large areas of West Africa", and that it is
a not uncommon cause of child delinquency, adult crime, and
beggary there.

In view of the uncertainty of finding trypanosomes in the
blood, glands, and cerebrospinal fluid, and of the great variability
of the physical signs (especially in the Gambian form and in the
field), Tooth's description of the mental symptoms are of especial
value to psychiatry and are therefore quoted at some length. He
states that "among Tryps. patients attending treatment centres
throughout the Gold Coast, gross lunacy occurs in approximately
8 per cent"—most often, in late cases, a euphoric dementia with
impulsive behaviour, and next most often, a chronic overactivity.
In the differential diagnosis from other organic psychoses, he
found such patients were seldom more restless by night than by
day. He examined 232 trypanosomiasis patients in the field and
found minor mental symptoms (not amounting to frank psychosis) in 194, or 84 per cent. This figure does not include
abnormal sleeping as a symptom; of this he found 63 per cent in
the series. An analysis of the mental symptoms in the 194 patients

mentioned disclosed the following as the main symptoms, in order of frequency: bad temper, 54 per cent; dull, forgetful, and dysphasic, 53 per cent; weeping, 41 per cent; vivid dreaming, 37 per cent; overtalking and talking nonsense, 30 per cent; hallucinosis, 22 per cent; and dirty and incontinent, 11 per cent. In this series he also found some neurological abnormality in 50 per cent, the commonest being tremors of the lips and tongue, increased deep tendon reflexes, and signs of cerebellar ataxia.

Tooth observes that "in general, there is some justification for describing the clinical picture of Tryps. as a combination of typically organic, and schizophrenic components", and he notes a resemblance to all types of schizophrenia—simple, catatonic, and paranoid—in mental, vasomotor, and endocrine symptoms.

Malaria

Malaria, usually subtertian, is endemic or hyperendemic throughout tropical Africa at all levels below about 5,500 feet and occurs at many places above. Garnham[107] has drawn attention to the fact that malarial statistics have declined in recent years all over East Africa but that it still constitutes one of the greatest problems there.

It impinges in different ways on different age groups. Thus, to summarize from Jeliffe,[137] in the first 6 months of life there is probably some transplacental immunity, at least to local parasites. The next 18 months are the most dangerous but, provided exposure to the same strain of subtertian malaria continues uninterruptedly, malaria is not usually a cause of severe ill health in later childhood. Where high endemicity is only seasonal, there are apt to be repeated bouts of fever, enlargement of the spleen, and some anaemia and general cachexia.

In adults the clinical manifestations of malaria depend largely on other factors. In immunized Africans of good general health and nutrition, the infection is of little significance; whereas in nonimmunes, and especially where the general health and nutrition are poor, the disease is dangerous to life. In chronic forms it gives rise to loss of appetite and weight, low irregular fever, general debility, and a varying anaemia.

Malaria is important in tropical psychiatry, and the present writer,[50] found it accounted for 3·4 per cent of first admissions to the mental hospital of Kenya. Its psychiatric importance depends on the facts that mental illness is more likely to supervene on a background of general debility; that confusional states may occur (as in other infections) from the bouts of fever; that malaria is probably the commonest cause of febrile convulsions in African children; and that the subtertian form is apt to be complicated by cerebral malaria. The last two points require some further discussion.

Osuntokun[194] made a valuable study of febrile convulsions in Nigeria. He defined "febrile convulsions" as convulsions caused by an extra-encephalic pyrexial or febrile illness, and found in a series of 155 children with such convulsions, that malaria was their commonest cause. It is most likely that some of these would sustain permanent brain damage.

Cerebral malaria is the most frequent severe complication of malaria. It is not very common in Africans (accounting for only 9 in a series of 2,000 autopsies seen by Gelfand,[111] and for 4·5 per cent of the 269 neurological cases seen by Muwazi and Trowell,[185] and for 3·6 per cent of the 727 neurological cases seen by Hutton[132]). Hutton says that "round Kampala cerebral malaria only occurs in the young children of the indigenous inhabitants, whereas the adult cases are invariably non-immune immigrants", an observation which may well be true for the whole country. Wright[268] draws attention to two main types of this illness, in the first of which, the capillaries of the brain may in heavy infections be blocked with the developing forms of the malarial parasite and which is usually associated with the gradual onset of coma; while in the second, an embolism of the parasites occurs and the onset of coma is sudden. Hutton[132] says that "patients frequently show disturbance of consciousness and may be retarded or psychotic for a period after recovery". Gelfand,[111] in describing the pathology of cerebral malaria, refers to blocking of subcortical capillaries with parasites, areas of focal necrosis, and later patches of sclerosis.

It seems quite likely therefore that some permanent mental impairment may sometimes follow cerebral malaria.

Pneumonia

Lobar pneumonia is exceedingly common and severe in Africans and is a frequent cause of delirious states which may so dominate the clinical picture that the pulmonary disease is not recognized at first. Thus, the present writer[50] found it accounted for 2·5 per cent of first admissions to the mental hospital of Kenya.

Broncho-pneumonia is common in the children and, as a cause

of febrile convulsions in these, Osuntokun[194] found it to be nearly as important as malaria, accounting for over one-fifth of the cases in his series.

Schistosomiasis

Monekosso[181] says of this disease: "Failure to control the snail hosts and failure to find effective and safe therapeutic drugs in the face of the spread of the disease (necessitated by much needed agricultural expansion) has brought this disease to second place (after malaria) among important infective diseases in Middle Africa."

Previously the ill-effects of schistosomiasis were attributed mainly to the anaemia resulting from the drain of blood from bladder or rectum, but it is likely that visceral involvement is the more important factor. It seems that in endemic areas there is some immunity up to about 3 years old when the child population is increasingly affected until, by about 15 years old, practically everyone has acquired it; thereafter a high prevalence persists till about the age of 30 years and then it falls till less than 30 per cent of the population are passing ova even in infected regions.

The debilitating effects of this infection on the growing child are difficult to disentangle from those of the several other infections that impinge on this age group. But to quote Gelfand[113]. "In the European whose nutritional state is good and who rarely suffers from more than one disease at a time a better picture of the toxic effects of bilharziasis can be obtained. In the stage when ova are still being excreted and the worms are therefore living, the school child lags behind, showing reduced powers of concentration, less interest in others and lack of endurance at games . . . It would be reasonable to argue that the African child is affected similarly."

Tuberculosis

"Tuberculosis", in Monekosso's[182] words, "remains one of the biggest clinical and epidemiological problems confronting Middle Africa today."

In general it seems to play a much larger part in neurology than in psychiatry in Africa. Pulmonary tuberculosis is much more commonly acute than in Europe, and Collomb[65] has remarked upon its importance in the aetiology of confusional states in Senegal.

It has, moreover, to be noted that tuberculous meningitis is quite frequent and, as elsewhere, its onset is insidious and it is apt to masquerade as mental illness; and that tuberculomas of the brain, large enough to dominate the clinical picture, though rare in Europe, are by no means so rare in Africans.

Encephalitis

Encephalitis of virus origin, and a variety of encephalopathies, are diagnosed from time to time and doubtless often not diagnosed as such but seen as mental illness. The present writer[50] found Parkinsonian symptoms in 1·6 per cent of his series of first admissions and believed that all of these were post-encephalitic.

Hutton[132] diagnosed acute encephalitis 28 times and acute encephalopathy 30 times in his series of 727 neurological cases in Uganda. He wrote: "The main difficulties in the diagnosis of encephalitis are the large number of conditions from which such diseases have to be differentiated. There are many toxic encephalopathic states of which the aetiology is uncertain which may give a similar picture. In addition, syphilitic meningo-encephalitis, cerebral malaria, trypanosomiasis, tuberculous meningitis, relapsing fever, all may need to be differentiated. With the difficulties of virus isolation in such cases during life their nature will tend to remain obscure."

Meningitis

Meningitis is frequent and, apart from local epidemics of cerebro-spinal fever, is most often due to the pneumococcus, and then to tuberculosis.

Other infections

There are in tropical Africa many other infections whose role in psychiatry is either occasional, as with relapsing fever, typhus, and yellow fever, or very indirect.

The latter are exemplified by hookworm, roundworm, tapeworms and the dysenteries. Their effects are insidiously debilitating and it may well be that malnutrition, to be discussed in the next section, is often more dependent on one of these infections (or on say malaria or tuberculosis) than it is on deficiencies in the diet as such.

*   *   *

These then are the infections of major importance for

pyschiatry—a mixed bag, with little in common other than their insidiously debilitating effects, which may be ephemeral but are often life-long. Few Africans are free from all of these, and it is easy to find examples of people infected concurrently with several, and who may or may not be complaining of ill-health. "Normality" in the African, even from the standpoint of infection alone, can thus be seen as a rather meaningless abstraction.

Nutritional Factors

Sherman and Lanford[226] say:

"Differences which are really nutritional have doubtless sometimes been attributed to racial factors was emphasized by Hopkins . . . in 1931. A community, he explained, may be found in equilibrium with an environment which includes its food supply, and the fact of such equilibrium has hitherto been taken as evidence that the environment supplies everything needed. Hence any inferiority was taken to be racial, whereas actually a racial potentiality of higher development may become manifest with an improvement in the food."

With certain notable exceptions, the great bulk of the African population south of the Sahara is mainly vegetable-eating. A few tribes, such as the Masai of East Africa, live largely on meat and milk. Other East African tribes keep cattle and goats mainly for purposes of currency and occasionally eat the meat, though they rarely use the milk. Other tribes living by the sea, the great lakes, or the few rivers consume much fish. For the rest, any sort of animal food is a rarity. As far as vegetables are concerned, the main staple foods in various parts are maize, millets, rice, cassava, sweet potatoes, yams, and plantains. Pulses and greenleaf vegetables are also eaten in various areas, but little fruit is consumed apart from bananas. Since vegetable food contains mainly potassium salts, sodium salts are usually deficient but are made up by the use of salt or salt-containing earths. Various condiments are added in small quantities. Native beer, made from fermented grain, and, in the West, palm wine, are widely consumed.

In regard to infancy, the African mother commonly receives no special food, yet breast-feeding is universal and continues for up to two or three years or even longer. Information concerning the quality of the milk is conflicting, but there is no doubt that the milk must be progressively deficient in quantity throughout the long period of breast-feeding and in relation to the needs of the growing child. Supplementary feeding is the rule from early months but is almost entirely carbohydrate in type. After weaning, the diet is gradually increased to adult standards, but is almost entirely carbohydrate and mainly starchy in type at first.

As to how far the food supply in tropical Africa meets the needs of the people is the subject of the rest of this section. In the first instance one has to consider the parts that the various food constituents play in human nutrition generally. These constituents are therefore considered in turn.

Proteins

The proteins supply energy, but their main function is for the growth and maintenance of the tissues themselves. There is a great variety of proteins, and their value in nutrition depends on their amino-acids. There are about 22 of these, of which 8 are indispensable in the diet since they cannot be synthesized in the body and yet (like the others) are required for tissue maintenance. Proteins are therefore called "complete" if they contain the 8 essential amino-acids and otherwise are called "incomplete". The proteins in many plant foods, for instance, lack some particular essential amino-acid such as lysine, tryptophane, or methionine. The concept of "completeness", however, is apt to be misleading since (*a*) no food consisting exclusively of the eight essential items would, in fact, be adequate; (*b*) incomplete proteins given in suitable combinations may recompense each other's deficiencies and be complete in effect; and (*c*) energy from carbohydrates and fats is also essential in protein synthesis in the tissues, as are certain vitamins and minerals.

From the point of view of practical adequacy, the best protein foods are eggs, meat, fish, and milk; of less value are pulses and cereals; and of least value are the starchy root vegetables and bananas. Animal proteins therefore hold first place and the need for these is greatest in the infant and growing child and in the pregnant and lactating mother. It is, in general, only too clear that an inadequacy of high-class protein in the diet is the rule throughout tropical and southern Africa, except among a few pastoral and fishing peoples.

Fats and carbohydrates

These two food constituents can be dealt with together since their functions are in some ways interchangeable and are largely concerned with the energy requirements of the body.

Fat is primarily a fuel storage material and, when food is taken in excess of calorie expenditure, the equivalent of the excess calories is deposited as fat. Fats supply about 9, and carbohydrates about 4, calories per gramme so that by volume the former are more economical. Dietetics in Europe and America tends to furnish between a quarter and a third of the total calories in the form of fat. There is a gross lack of fats, both animal and vegetable, in most African diets.

In regard to carbohydrates, and in the words of Soskin and Levine[235]: "Carbohydrate resembles fat in being a fuel material but differs from fat in that it is an indispensable one. The tissues of the body constantly require and use carbohydrate under all physiologic conditions. Even a temporary fall in the blood sugar below certain critical levels is accompanied by serious disability. Nevertheless, the amount of carbohydrate present in the body at any one time is very small. This amount, if it were not replaced as used, could sustain life for only a fraction of one day."

In effect, in view of the slight possibility of carbohydrate storage in the body, especially when there is little development of adipose tissue, the carbohydrate acts as a sparer of protein and, in the presence of a carbohydrate deficiency, an excessive break-down of tissue protein must occur.

By and large, it seems that calorie requirements are usually met, but with little to spare. This, however, is not the whole story. Nutritional factors never act in isolation from each other and, as will appear later in this section, a proper balance between calorie and protein intake is probably the most important aspect of the problem.

Minerals

Calcium and phosphorus, ingested in a suitable ratio, and in the presence of vitamin D, are largely concerned in the metabolism of bone, though they have other less obvious functions. Calcium needs are especially high in later pregnancy and lactation, and in infancy. The chief sources of calcium are animal foods and vegetable leaves, and of phosphorus, animal foods and vegetable seeds;

but, although most of the foodstuffs richest in these are in short supply in Africa, it seems that the intake is usually adequate.

Iron is largely concerned in the formation of haemoglobin, and its lack results in anaemia. Tissue iron is well conserved, excretion is slight, and bodily needs are met by controlled absorption, so that in health, apart from pregnancy, lactation, growth, and menstruation, little iron is required. African foodstuffs therefore probably contain a sufficiency of iron for most purposes; but, as will be shown later, they are inadequate for the needs of the breast-fed infant. It seems that the low haemoglobin levels almost constantly encountered in the rural African at all ages are, except in infancy, due mainly to concomitant infections, protein lack, and liver disease, iron inadequacy being only relative to these.

Sodium is lacking in most vegetable foods where its place is taken by potassium. The deficiency of salt in African diets is, however, usually compensated by access to salt-containing earths or by the buying of salt.

The other essential minerals are apparently seldom dietetic problems in Africa. Potassium and magnesium are in good supply, and iodine lack is not a general problem though goitre occurs sporadically and in several endemic foci.

Vitamins

Vitamin A is needed, according to Clausen,[60] "to maintain the structure and function of certain of the specialized epithelial and glandular tissues, the visual functions of the retina, and the growth of the body". The specific manifestations of its deficiency in man are night blindness, xerophthalmia, and phrynoderma; other manifestations, which may in particular cases arise from a variety of other causes, are retardation of growth and lowered resistance to infection. The vitamin itself occurs only in animal foods, but its precursors, which are converted to vitamin A in the body, are abundant in green leaves, tubers and fruits, and are deficient in cereals. Over large areas of the continent, diets contain little enough of vitamin A or its precursors and the British Committee on Nutrition in the Colonial Empire[121] recorded a widespread deficiency in African territories.

Vitamin D regulates the metabolism of calcium and phosphorus in the body, and in its absence the supply of these elements to the skeleton falls short of requirements and rickets or osteomalacia results. Vitamin D occurs principally in animal fats and, as its precursors, in a variety of vegetable foods. The precursors are converted to vitamin D in the body by the action of ultra-violet light on the skin. The vitamin is grossly deficient in most African foodstuffs, but this deficiency is usually remedied by the sunlight. Rickets on the whole is rare in tropical Africa though it has been described in Tanganyika and Sierra Leone.

Vitamin C plays a part in the formation of connective tissues, in the metabolism of certain amino-acids and in resistance to infection. Its lack results in lassitude, irritability and bodily weakness, and later in gingivitis and a variety of haemorrhagic manifestations; in infancy, bony lesions also occur. Vitamin C is found especially in fruits and green vegetables, and there are probably appreciable amounts in most African condiments and beers. Grain foods are deficient and, except in areas, such as Uganda, where the staple food is plantains or bananas, the consumption of this vitamin must be relatively low throughout Africa. Scurvy in classical forms is, however, reported only occasionally.

Vitamin B complex consists of several known factors and others which have not yet been isolated. Even the precise role of some of the known factors in human dietetics and human metabolism is still too uncertain for discussion in a work of this scope. However, there remain three factors—thiamine, riboflavine, and niacin—whose role is sufficiently clear and of obvious importance for this study. Regarding these three especially, and before proceeding to their separate description, it is, however, pertinent to record Soskin and Levine's[235] reference to "the fallacy of regarding any single factor of the B complex as more important than another, for the normal chain of events (in carbohydrate metabolism) can be broken by a lack of any one of them".

Thiamine (with riboflavine and niacin) plays an essential part in the metabolism of carbohydrate, so that it must be consumed in quantities related to the carbohydrate intake. Signs of its deficiency are most manifest in muscular tissue, including the myocardium, and in the central nervous system. In human subjects deprived of this factor alone there develop gastro-intestinal symptoms, signs of myocardial weakness, polyneuritic syndromes, and symptoms of organic neurasthenia or even mild confusional or paranoid states. The vitamin is seldom deficient in the diet, but bodily deficiency may sometimes arise from failure of absorption (in intestinal disease) or of storage (in liver disease).

Riboflavine is a constituent of a number of enzyme systems

associated with the intermediate metabolism of food, particularly of carbohydrates, and is probably also intimately concerned in protein metabolism. Its deficiency in man is characterized by cheilosis, angular stomatitis, glossitis, scrotal dermatitis, and a variety of eye lesions and visual disturbances. Signs of riboflavine deficiency are often associated with those of pellagra. Riboflavine is widely distributed in animal and vegetable foodstuffs but lacking in cereals, and signs of its deficiency are common in Africans.

Niacin, like riboflavine, plays an essential part in human carbohydrate and protein metabolism. Indeed their distinguishing roles are not precisely defined and, as Sherman and Lanford[226] say: "The typical pellagrin is usually a sufferer from shortage not only of niacin but also of riboflavine". In niacin deficiency there occurs a variety of symptoms in the skin (with a characteristic rash) the alimentary tract (with glossitis, stomatitis, nausea and perhaps diarrhoea), and the nervous system (with tremors, rigidity, symptoms of polyneuritis, and organic neurasthenia or more serious mental disturbances). These three systems are not necessarily all involved at once, so that mental symptoms may dominate the clinical picture. Niacin occurs in many animal and vegetable foodstuffs, but is especially lacking in maize. Moreover, gastro-intestinal or liver disease may interfere with its assimilation.

These are the food constituents of major importance in tropical Africa and it has to be re-emphasized that they do not act in isolation from each other, but that their proper balance in the diet is as important as their individual adequacy.

The problem is therefore far from simple and is further complicated in Africa in a variety of ways. Thus, in each area there is usually one staple foodstuff which forms the bulk of the diet and may differ from the staple foodstuff in nearby areas. The diet is highly dependent on the seasons and, though adequate at one time, may at other times be inadequate. It is uncertain how far tropical conditions modify dietetic needs. In places where certain items are in good supply, these sources may not be tapped; thus where cows are plentiful the milk may not be drunk, and Forde and Jones,[98] for instance, say that fishing is forbidden in parts of Nigeria since fishes are believed to embody the souls of ancestors. The best food may be kept for the men, or for guests. A diet which may appear adequate may not be so on account of liver disease, of infestation with roundworms, or of other intestinal diseases which interfere with absorption or storage. Finally, the science of dietetics in other parts of the world was based on fairly well-defined clinical entities, such as rickets and scurvy, in populations which were, in the main, well fed but lacked some essential item. It is different in Africa, where deficiencies are commonly multiple and are further obscured by infectious disease.

It remains therefore to discuss the question of malnutrition as this is seen in Africa.

The classical deficiency diseases, with the exception of pellagra, are all decidedly rare. Thus rickets, beri-beri, and scurvy occur only sporadically or in small foci, and even pellagra seems to play no dramatic part in psychiatric practice here. Anaemia due entirely to a deficiency of iron in the diet is also probably rare.

Many of the minor symptoms indicative of a deficiency of vitamin A or of some member of the vitamin B group are commonly seen at all ages, as are a variety of malnutritional states dependent as much on concomitant infections as on dietary inadequacy.

Outstandingly important among malnutritional illnesses throughout tropical Africa, however, is protein-calorie malnutrition, known in its advanced forms as "kwashiorkor". This condition appears to be the outcome of a diet that is very poor in protein but over-rich in calories. It afflicts particularly the children during the second to the fourth years of their lives, and occurs particularly in areas where the staple foods are mainly starchy and where cereals, pulses, and animal proteins play little part. It seems to stem, however, not so much from a lack of the basic food constituents in the country, as from faulty feeding of the infants and small children. For, as Dean[80] has emphasized, "In East Africa generally, the chief nutritional problem is the satisfaction of the need for protein in the diets of recently weaned children. The children are usually given only those parts of the adult diet that seem to be most easily digested—the staples such as plantains, sweet potatoes, cassava or maize—and do not, therefore, receive enough protein, or enough protein of good quality."

In Uganda this illness is so common that Dean and Burgess,[81] following a survey of 5 districts there, were able to say: "It is probable that well over 2,000 cases of advanced malnutrition occur each year in the Kingdom. It would not surprise us if the true figure were much higher".

Finally, as Jelliffe[137] has pointed out, the baby is often probably at a nutritional disadvantage from the start since his mother did not obtain a sufficiency of protein during pregnancy.

Since the main interest of kwashiorkor for the theme of this book is the possibility that, impinging as it does on the child at a time of life when the brain is still rapidly developing, it may imperil this development, there is no need to describe its physical symptoms. There are, however, characteristic mental symptoms and these will be described in the chapter on psychology.

Cultural Factors

A fundamental fact of human life is that man is a social animal and, in the words of Mead,[178] "submitted throughout his entire individual existence to systematic cultural pressures" which elaborate, ignore, or suppress his developmental potentialities on different lines in different cultures.

Those cultural factors which seem to be most important for psychological development will be described in turn, as far as practicable in the chronological order in which they impinge upon the individual from birth to death. This is not only a convenient way of assembling the facts, but it is also appropriate to present them in the order of their importance, for it is doubtless generally true that the environment plays a diminishing role with advancing age in the moulding of personality. Moreover, the various facets of a culture impinge most effectively on the developing mind at different periods of life. Certain factors, such as ethics and magic, are not wholly amenable to this approach since they are influential throughout most of life and interlink inseparably with each other and with other factors. But, on the whole, this approach is a practicable one.

Something must next be said on the subject of dealing with the cultural factors as though these were uniform throughout the African countries that are being discussed. There is, of course, much cultural diversity throughout sub-Saharan Africa; each tribe is culturally unique in some degree, as was stressed by several speakers at the CCTA/CSA Symposium at Tananarive[56]. It is, however, the present writer's contention that, although there are probably few tribal groups for whom the description that follows is true in *all* its details there is a place for both particular and broad approaches and there is enough in common throughout this area, and as distinct from conditions that obtain in Europe, to justify a description at this degree of breadth.

African life is rapidly changing. The rising generations are adopting alien ways with alacrity and rapidly losing their own. The picture that emerges here is often therefore no longer typical. However, in so far as African culture does still exist and does differ from European, it does so on the lines described. The problem of "transition" is one which will be considered separately at the end of this chapter.

Finally, the description that follows may give the impression that African culture is entirely odd; alien to anything one knows in the Western world. This impression would be false. In this chapter, however, it is relevant to emphasize the peculiarities and it must be assumed that life is otherwise much like that in rural Europe.

The infant

Children are much wanted in African life. They are regarded as carrying a part of the soul or spirit of some forbear, commonly a grandparent of the same sex, and thus maintaining the family's immortality. Indeed, since some are likely to die young, it is safest to have several. Especially are they wanted by the mother, since the bearing of children enhances her status and, polygyny being the general rule, maintains her prestige with other wives. Barrenness is indeed the greatest affliction that can happen in her life.

The infant from the time it is born therefore receives its mother's whole-hearted affection. He is fed at the breast "on demand" and up to the age of at least 18 months, and often up to 2 or 3 years, or even longer. For most of this time he is in close physical contact with his mother, night and day—being carried either on her back or at her side, and is handled with confidence. The bond with her is further enhanced by the fact that a sexual taboo is strictly observed between the parents throughout most of this period; and the mother becomes highly sensitive to her child's needs and desires.

In the early years toilet training is lax to the point of non-existence, and the infant is encouraged to crawl, walk, talk, control his excretory functions, and act in general very much as and when he shows the inclination to do so himself. Discipline and punishment are hardly encountered at this time of life.

Supplementary feeding is commonly begun within a few weeks of birth and, contrary to the general permissiveness, the child may even be forced to imbibe a variety of foods which may seem digestible but, in the later periods at least, are often nutritionally inadequate.

As Collomb[67] has emphasized, in Senegal the child at this stage is never alone. Even if the mother is absent the child is in constant and intimate contact with relations who speak to him, hold him, and play with him.

The time of weaning is related to the time of lifting of the taboo on sexual intercourse since it is effected forthwith when the mother knows the next child is on the way. The degree of its abruptness has been subject to argument, but rather depends on whether one is viewing the matter from a physiological or a psychological angle. From a nutritional point of view it is clearly gradual, since in the later periods of breast-feeding the child was receiving most of his food from other sources. From the child's point of view, however, it is abrupt, often dramatically so. For all at once the almost continuous and totally permissive contact that he previously experienced with his mother comes to an end. Her attention is now thoroughly focused on the problems of her next pregnancy, the child is relegated to the care of other relations—grandparents, aunts, and elder siblings—and he is often subjected to some teasing by the latter at this time.

The child

A word must first be said about African relationships since they govern so much of the child's behaviour from an early age. Kenyatta,[143] referring to the Kikuyu says: "First and foremost he is several people's relative and several people's contemporary" and "It is with personal relations, rather than with natural phenomena, that the Kikuyu education is concerned right from the very beginning". His remarks would be equally applicable to most parts of Africa.

Since polygyny is the rule, the child is likely sooner or later to have a number of half-brothers and sisters besides his full ones. Ultimately he has relationships not only with his father and the latter's relations, and with his mother and her relations, but with the families of his father's other wives. Grades of seniority are recognized throughout, modes of address are varied appropriately in regard to each relationship, and the matter is still further complicated by the fact that, when a man dies, his wife becomes attached to the household of one of his male relations. The child's life thus becomes increasingly one of reciprocal relationships within an expanding community. After weaning he falls much under the influence of grandparents, uncles and aunts—whom he learns to address as father and mother—and elder siblings.

His education is particularly directed towards inculcating codes of manners, deportment, and behaviour in regard to his relations to a far remove. He has to learn many names and degrees of relationship since his behaviour patterns must be adjusted to each social context. Thus his behaviour in the presence of, say, his father's sister, is governed not so much on the basis of her own unique personality as by her peculiar relationship to himself. Indeed, in Kenyatta's[143] words: "In all tribal education the emphasis lies on a particular act of behaviour in a concrete situation." Much learning is by unconscious assimilation of the patterns of the group one age-step ahead but, in so far as teaching is explicit, it is by a variety of people—parents, older children, and other relations. Thus parental influence is much less exclusive than it usually is in Europe, but education is given by a variety of people, including the parents, whose influence is similar, since they themselves were all products of the same process.

There is, of course, no reading and writing, and the child is highly dependent for his amusement and his learning on the spoken word. Much teaching is done by the telling of stories, of folk-tales and myths; and ridicule for folk who make fools of themselves plays a large part in these. Tales with a moral are common and inculcate pride in the ancestors and clan. Above all, instruction is directed to the learning of proper manners and deportment in the presence of one's elders. The importance of integration within the group and the evils of solitude are stressed, and when Raum,[217] writing of Chaga childhood said, "The child becomes conditioned to a morality whose demands become less stringent the remoter they are from the 'initial situation' of the family", he said something that has much truth throughout Africa.

There is a high general level of knowledge of the world in several fields: in agriculture, animal husbandry, and hut-building for instance; and this knowledge is imparted to the child in due course. But causation, where this is unknown, is explained on magical and animistic lines, and this will be discussed later.

The father's relations with his child are remote at first, though he is important as an ideal, and punishment by him is used as a threat for misdemeanours. Punishment itself varies very much from tribe to tribe. It may take a corporal form, or the form of withholding of food, but it does not seem to include the threat of love-withdrawal, as Krige has suggested to the present writer. Threats, tales of bogey-men, and warnings of the curse of some relative or ancestor play a part in the maintenance of discipline. But perhaps the most powerful of all the modes of effecting conformity is the practice of ridicule by both the parental generation and the peer group.

Playtime and games are not organized by the parents and take the form, as one might expect, of imitation of adult activities, and of songs and dances. Toys and dolls, other than those crudely made by the children themselves, are conspicuous by their absence in Africa, and do not include such things as building blocks, jigsaw puzzles, and the host of mechanical objects (keys, switches, taps, etc.) that play so large a part in urban environments.

Sex play is also common, for the children quickly gain knowledge of adult sexual behaviour and imitate it among themselves, and masturbation is not discouraged in childhood.

In general it can be said that, although a variety of people play several roles in the education of the child, these roles are never mutually contradictory. As in all homogeneous, slowly changing cultures, each instructor—be he a grandfather, an uncle, or an elder brother—carries, as Mead[177] has emphasized, the same cultural assumptions. Each new piece of learning, no matter from whom it is received, is part of a comprehensive pattern in which the child's past, his present, and his future are all familiar and assumed.

Surprisingly early the children are expected to contribute to the life of the family, and the Westerner is often astonished to see little girls carrying babies on their backs and little boys, spear in hand, guarding their flocks. Childhood, in African theory, is a period of complete irresponsibility; and offences committed at this age are commuted by the parents. Yet, by European standards, African children are highly responsible. Indeed they may often be seen, by the age of 10 years or so, sitting with their elders and even taking part in the conversation with confidence and effect.

The adolescent

All societies throughout the world, literate or non-literate, recognize some sort of grading by age. In Africa, however, age-grading is often a highly formalized institution, and at no time is this more clearly seen than at puberty.

The initiation ceremonies, which are so widespread throughout Africa, mark both explicitly and symbolically the transition from childhood to maturity and, for the boys, the final detachment from the tutelage of women and admission to the company and pursuits of men. They form for the initiates the most dramatic and memorable experience of their lives. The details vary greatly from area to area but, in general, the rites are symbolic of death and rebirth, and the period is one of intense education in which certain elders instruct the initiates in the tribal folk-lore, traditions, magical beliefs and practices, moral codes, and sex-life. During initiation the pupils are kept in a state of excitement by the drama of the ritual; much of the language used in speech and song is bizarre and mystical, the manner of the instruction often counting for much more than its content. The ceremonies commonly include circumcision of the boys and an operation on the girls which varies from a slight ritual incision to a total excision of the labia minora and clitoris.

These initiatory ceremonies mark the advancement of the adolescent to responsible membership of the larger group or tribe, with the increase of rights and duties that this entails; at the same time, they act as a final reminder that this advancement is only partial and that his status is still subordinate to that of the parental generation.

Whereas, prior to initiation, masturbation was considered right and proper, thereafter it is regarded as childish, and intercourse between the sexes is correct. Even children are familiar with the sexual facts of life but at the time of initiation, instruction is explicit and detailed. Thereafter, sex-intercourse between members of the same age-group, though restricted in various ways (both as to the people involved and the procedure itself), is encouraged. Thus the members of one age-group come to regard each other as being in a special relationship, within which they must, among other things, love and marry. This relationship is grafted horizontally on the vertical lineage relationships and entails affiliations throughout the larger group.

The adult

The ambition felt by most men everywhere to wed and rear a family is enhanced in the African by the concept that his own spiritual immortality is closely linked with the future of his offspring. Therefore, sooner or later, one woman is chosen as his wife. The choice is seldom his, however; and, as Laubscher[155] says of a South African tribe, "Romance has its place in the love life of the Tembu but not in relation to marriage. Young men and girls have their love-affairs but these seldom, if ever, end in matrimony". For the purpose of marriage a "bride-price" (lobolo) must be paid. This institution, far from being a mere "buying" of, and humiliation to, the woman, is a stabilizing influence in African marriage and contributes to the respect with which the bride is held by her husband and his group. The attitude towards marriage is rather different from that which prevails among Europeans, since in Africa this institution is based more frankly on motives of economy and succession. Jeffreys[138] says, "There is ample evidence to show that marriage among the Negro is not so much a personal affair as an inter-family or group affair", and, "the fundamental conception behind all lobolo transactions is that lobolo is the child-price", and is thereby a means of ensuring rights in forthcoming children to the husband. Marriage is thus a civil contract in which both parties commit themselves to certain obligations to the other, but in which they both also maintain a considerable autonomy.

Polygyny is the rule for, apart from the question of children, it is the women who work in the fields and, if a man is successful and acquires much land, this work cannot be done by one woman. Prestige attaches to being the wife of a man with several wives; the first wife often chooses the subsequent wives and jealousy, when it occurs, is most likely to arise from barrenness, which is the greatest calamity that can befall an African woman. Thanks to polygyny and the inheritance of widows, prostitution is probably non-existent in indigenous life. Adultery, especially by the woman, is regarded as serious (as breaking certain taboos); but since some licence is permitted for wives in various circumstances, the word "adultery" carries connotations which are different from those among Europeans. Illegitimacy has little meaning in Africa, for children born out of wedlock "always belong", in Laubschers[155] words, "to some male, either the man who pro-created them or the mother's father", if indeed they are not accepted as his by the husband.

There is a considerable specialization of labour between the sexes, the men among other activities doing the bush-clearing and cattle-herding (if cattle are kept), while the women hoe the fields, collect the firewood, cook the food, and particularly in West Africa, indulge in commerce in the markets. There are also a few major occupational specialities (such as ironsmiths) and several categories of medicine men with much esoteric knowledge of herbs and treatments of the people's physical and mental ills.

Compared with Europe, however, specialization is relatively slight, and every adult is in a high degree familiar with the whole culture of his group. There is thus a high level of general know-ledge, and a wide understanding of agricultural phenomena; many names of natural objects are memorized and the average man's vocabulary is extensive. The African loves conversation and discussion, and is often eloquent, and frequently a gifted linguist. Music and the dance also play a large part in his life and thanks to the general participation, powers of extemporization in these arts are not limited to the few. Gorer,[120] who had an opportunity to witness many dances in West Africa and compare them with those of various southern Asian peoples, said of the latter that they "dance more subtly, more dramatically; but as far as I have seen their range is limited and their invention small compared with the Negroes". A distinguished student of African music, Tracey,[246] speaking of the part music plays in communities throughout Africa, goes so far as to say that, with a few tribal exceptions, "home-made African music is one of the most important of all the integrating factors in their social life". Song and dance, though they also have their set times and places, are not, however, confined to these but form a frequent background to African life and are even regarded as a stimulus for labour. Indeed, it is nothing rare to see a line of carriers, at the end of an exhausting march, enter the camp leaping and singing as though this were the gladsome dawn of day and not the nightfall.

As Gluckman[117] has emphasized, there is a considerable empir-ical knowledge to explain events, but each event in which men are involved is only thus partially explained, for there seems also to be much of the fortuitous, and it is this latter part which is explained in magical-animistic lines.

Magic, in Parrinder's[197] words, "is an attempt at manipulating the energy of the world, invisible but potent. In this it resembles science, and has often been called an elementary science. But magicians believe in spiritual forces which they can call up at will. To distinguish magic from higher forms of religion it may be said that magic deals with impersonal forces, while the gods and ancestors are personal. The magician tries to harness these impersonal forces to his purposes, by incantation and rite." Magic thus provides in crises of life both an explanation and a course of action. Strictly speaking, however, it is not an elementary science since it is not subject to verification or criticism, but is fixed and ritualized. It can be used for good or evil. Everywhere it has its professional exponents, and a multitude of protective charms are sold in every market.

"Witchcraft", to quote Parrinder[197] again, "is believed in as widely in Africa as it was in Europe during the Middle Ages and Renaissance times. Basically it is the belief that human souls are stolen and destroyed by witches who fly by night to cannibalistic assemblies. . . . The reason for this belief is the need to explain mysterious diseases . . . and in particular the many sicknesses that kill young children suddenly." Odhalo,[188] writing of the Luo of East Africa, says: "Evil spirits abound in the environment ready to pounce on the unsuspecting victim. The most susceptible are infants and children, the rich, or whoever tries to be above others, women during their pregnancy or while giving birth, and engaged couples . . . susceptible persons must call on a witch-doctor for advice and necessary precautions. The witch-doctors are consulted by all classes of people from the most illiterate to the most educated."

On the subject of religion, Parrinder[197] says: "The late Edwin Smith . . . compared African religion to a triangle. At the apex is the Supreme Being; on either side are great spiritual powers, nature gods and ancestors, some more powerful in one place than in another; at the base of the triangle are the magical charms and amulets which are believed to be vehicles of spiritual force." Referring to the various spiritual forces that constitute the religious background of African life Parrinder goes on to say: "The many forces are recognized to be of different strength and arranged in a hierarchy. This may fairly be described as 'poly-theism'. This word means belief in many gods and it can by extension include the ancestors as well. This is not a perfect description, for it does not define the position of the supreme God. But then his place varies in the belief of different areas. Some think of God as very near and pour libations to him, while others consider him remote and rarely refer to him."

Religion in most parts of the modern world is much associated with particular places of worship, churches and temples; and with particular times, days of the week, and religious anniversaries; and tends in general to be set apart in time and place from a life that is otherwise "secular". This is not the case in Africa. Temples are rare and the spirit world, whether one of nature spirits, as in West and Equatorial Africa, or of ancestral spirits, as in East and Southern Africa, is hardly separable for the African from the rest of his life.

It has also to be said, however, that indigenous religions are essentially tribal and that the spirit world envisaged is closely attached to the tribal land, with little interest beyond it. Morality depends on the application or contravention of the traditionally correct rules of behaviour, and its enforcement depends on a public opinion which gains strength from the fact that each man is well known to all the people in his neighbourhood. The aim of justice is not so much punishment of an individual as the assessment of compensation by the offending to the injured group and, since the rules are quite well known to all, their infringement implies unsocial motives, and intent can be assumed.

Throughout the fabric of African culture there runs the thread of participation in the life of the community. This thread is not broken by death, and the remembered ancestors are conceived as continuing for a time to play the part they played in life. Among the Nilotic Jaluo, for instance, as described by Carman and Roberts,[48] the ancestral spirits are even provided with a little hut within the family compound. In times of family crisis, these ancestors will be approached and supplication made for their assistance. As grown men have more "power" than boys, and old people more power than grown men, so the spirits of the deceased have still more power and may be assumed to wish to use it for the succour of their offspring.

The aged

For the elders and the aged there is an honoured place.

Prestige rises with age and the highest prestige, apart from the remembered ancestors, attaches to old age, for which also there are well-defined rights and duties. Since reinforcement and consolidation of memories of past experience and prefiguring of future experience are characteristic of slowly changing cultures as Mead[177] has emphasized, preparedness for old age is inherent in the whole process. And indeed, unlike what commonly happens in urban Europe, the longer one lives the better one understands one's world. Moreover, the mere fact of having lived so long in so magic-ridden a world is proof in itself of the "power" of one's spirit.

The elders confer in all matters affecting the welfare of the group; and the aged, thought of as having one foot in the grave, are thus regarded as the highest authority in affairs of the spirits and the fittest intermediaries in all approaches to the ancestors.

This leads to the subject of death. Bereavement is not borne in isolation. Ritual lamentation, in which many relations take part, is the rule. A failure to take part would give rise to suspicions of having poisoned the deceased. These lamentations may be prolonged for days and to the point of exhaustion. They serve, not only to share and ease any distress that may be felt, but often, as Prince[209] has shown, to give reassurance by the nature of the rituals of the deceased's continued existence, and also to propitiate the deceased for any malevolent thoughts one may previously have harboured in regard to him. When these proceedings come to an end, the participants resume the tenor of their lives as though there had been no bereavement.

Finally, the culture described is in each tribal area a functional unit. This unit cannot develop in a geographical vacuum but must be attached to particular areas of land, to which all customs, myths, history, and religion refer; which give all life, and which nurse the ancestral spirits. No such study as this would therefore be complete without this final emphasis on the land, for when African culture loses its roots in the soil, it quickly disintegrates.

The African in transition

Transition in Africa is a large subject which can only be considered summarily here.

To say that a society is in a state of transition is to say little enough. Europeans are familiar with change; it is indeed virtually the order of the day. Even within the lifetime of many there have not only been great changes in material things but in the whole conception of the universe. Thus, within a few decades, the solid world of Newtonian physics has melted into a more fluid world of probabilities; religious faith (judging from church attendance) has drastically declined; and the internal combustion engine has taken over from the horse. Up to a point, however, Europeans are prepared for change. Their education has been of a nature to encourage curiosity in first principles and, in so far as they are representative of a culture that prides itself on competition and initiative, they not only expect great changes in their time but even delight in searching for new fields to conquer.

Even so, Europeans and Americans are no strangers to the evils of transition and it seems appropriate to quote Faris[92] here on the subject of behaviour disorders in the industrial cities of America, he says:

"Such research of a scientific character as has dealt with the relation between ecology and behaviour has mainly been concerned with social disorganization and the consequent forms of personal disorganization. This disorganization is for the most part a phenomenon of a great transition. . . . Such movements break up the social systems that control and integrate the behaviour of persons, so that new, unconventional and abnormal types of behaviour appear. These abnormalities are not essentially aspects of city life, or civilized society, but rather of the populations which are changing from one system to another."

The shock in Africa is very much greater. African societies have presumably never been quite static; no utterly static organization could survive for long. But it is of the essence of all traditional cultures that their survival depends on gradualness of change, for a drastic alteration of any of their major components is likely to disintegrate the whole.

As regards the nature of the impact from outside Africa, it is commonly said that the major factors have been missionary influence and education on European lines. The present writer would dispute this, and was led to do so in his study[53] of the Mau Mau rebellion in Kenya. The indigenous African's approach to life was largely governed by the question of "power". He saw the world around him as a battlefield populated by conflicting

forces. Quite apart from supernatural aspects, but always reinforced by these, he saw in the real world dangerous beasts
imbued with power to harm; alien and inevitably hostile tribes;
successful men within his group who had achieved their ends
(usually at the expense of others) by reason of the power within
them. He saw his own survival and possible success as an
outcome of some power in him or of some other source of
power that might be tapped through, say, the witch-doctor. In
indigenous life a balance was achieved between these powers, the
tribe as a whole maintained its strength, and the tribal culture
itself remained unshaken. All that was changed by conquest. The
invaders were seen as possessed of powers of a different order,
which must accordingly be tapped.

It is believed therefore that, wherever the arrival of the alien was
crowned with success, and that alien (be he a soldier, an
administrator, a trader, a missionary, or some other) was able to
maintain a strong position, the local culture was doomed precisely
in the degree of his success and the extension of his influence. It is
the material success of the immigrant which is first recognized and
which sounds the death knell of the earlier culture. The influence
of the missioner and educator is governed, at first, by the degree in
which he is seen as representative of that material power and not
(again at first) by his educational influence as such.

The chief ways in which transition has affected the African can
be considered under the five environmental headings earlier
described.

The first four can be dealt with quite shortly. Geography and
climate have not changed, though new modes of dress and
footwear have sometimes altered their impact. Infections have
been combated with tremendous effect. Largely due to this there
has been a vast increase of population. Thus in Kenya alone the
African population has risen from about $2\frac{1}{2}$ million in 1923 to
nearly $9\frac{1}{2}$ million in 1966. The effects of this in modifying the
manner of life are as great as they are unforeseeable. Nutrition
has not always improved, especially for the children, due to the
growing of crops for sale on plots that were previously devoted
to the growing of the families' food, yet which are no bigger
than before.

In regard to the cultural factors, the alien influences undermine
the whole extended family system and all the behaviour patterns
that are based on this. Whereas work was previously a family

affair in which each person played his part in and for the family, it now becomes a matter of jobs done outside the family solely for monetary rewards to the workman as an individual. Since on the whole it is the boys, rather than the girls, who go to school and learn the alien ways, and the men who go away to work, a divergence of interests and of ways of thinking often develops between the sexes and further undermines the solidarity of the family. The traditional religions, dependent on the worship of nature spirits and on homage to the ancestors; religions, which in their turn were closely attached to the ancestral land, decline and their place is often taken, especially in South Africa, by a multitude of independent churches. Magic and witchcraft, on the other hand survive and even blossom for, as Gluckman[117] has stressed, their techniques are more adaptable to the new situation than are most other elements of the traditional culture. Whether or not they actually increase, as suggested by Marwick (1956), is an open question, but it is clear that, with the loss of the other cultural, and particularly the religious elements, they are no longer held in check. Perhaps, most importantly, an "eye culture" is being substituted for an "ear culture", but this will receive extended consideration at a later stage.

On the theme of the effects of rapid culture change on mental health, Raman's thought-provoking article[214] calls for reference here. It refers to the rather different, racially mixed population of Mauritius, but is entirely relevant to the situation in Africa, or indeed in many parts of the world today. He found that it was not so much the rapidity of the deculturative and acculturative process which was damaging, as the lack of uniformity in its distribution. He found that the members of the first generation to be subjected to this process, fared much better than those of the second, for the former had assimilated the essence of the original culture in their formative years, whereas the latter not only had not done so, but found themselves projected into a world where a variety of value systems prevailed, and where they searched in vain for groups with which to identify.

Finally, some African Cultures appear to be less vulnerable than others. Thus some pastoral societies, such as the Masai in Kenya, are very resistant to outside influences; and some of the more highly organized peoples of West Africa, particularly where they have spontaneously developed an urban way of living, such as the Yoruba of Nigeria, are better able to assimilate the alien ways without disruption of their own.

But, by and large, African peoples have shown a great avidity to acquire the alien ways and most of the Africans one meets today are in a highly transitional state. So much so indeed that it is becoming increasingly difficult to say how far characteristics that the European observer regards as peculiarly African refer to a personality that is the outcome of the traditional culture or to one that is not.

In illustration of this, the present writer[51] made an attempt 20 years ago to study the ways in which Africans default, often exasperatingly, in their working relationships with Europeans. Thirty-three examples of unreliable behaviour by African employees were collected, and it was commented that, although failures such as these occur from time to time in employees in Europe, they would only be frequent there in persons who would be considered thoroughly irresponsible, whereas Africans who do not frequently default in ways like these are rather exceptional people. In studying the basis of these failures, the chief finding (occurring in all but 3 or 4 of the examples) was a failure to see an event as an element in a total situation. Thus, as one of the examples, a number of mental hospital patients and their attendants were playing football when one patient escaped and *all* the attendants (and some of the patients) chased him leaving the rest of the patients unattended.

How far an inability to deal with "total situations" such as this in the transitional world is an outcome of something characteristic of indigenous psychology, or is merely a trap that a European might fall into when visiting, say, China or the planet Mars, is a problem for consideration in the chapter on psychology.

Physical Disease

Physical illnesses will be discussed only in so far as they have any peculiar interest for African psychology or psychiatry.

Genetic Disease

Sickle-cell anaemia

To quote an admirably succinct passage from an article by Mahmood:[164] "Sickle cell anaemia ('SS') is a disorder caused by the complete replacement of the normal haemoglobin 'A' by an abnormal haemoglobin 'S'. It is a homozygous inherited condition, i.e. a gene for Hb S is donated by both the parents (who, in the present East African context, almost always carry sickle-cell trait—'AS', but are rarely 'SS'). Such AS parents may have a normal AA child (probability 1 in 4), an SS child (probability 1 in 4), or an AS child (probability 1 in 2)."

The trait (AS condition) is quite rare south of the Zambesi river, but occurs with varying frequency throughout tropical Africa, being commoner in the west (23 per cent in Nigeria), and is probably most frequent among the Pygmies in whom a figure of 45 per cent was obtained. Indeed the abnormal gene may derive from the Pygmies for the reasons given in Chapter 1. Possessors of the trait (AS) are probably partially protected against the more serious complications of subtertian malaria, though not against acquiring this infection.

Sufferers from the anaemia (SS condition) are subject to crises which are most often thrombotic in origin. The thromboses affect particularly the bones and joints, but may affect the brain. The disease may vary somewhat in its symptomatology in various areas and French writers, particularly, have emphasized the neurological manifestations. Thus Gallais and Charlopain's[103] list of these includes various pains and paraesthesiae, vertigo, convulsions, cranial nerve palsies, aphasia, meningeal syndromes, hemiplegias and mental confusion.

Colour blindness and myopia

Among 537 Bantu (Baganda) males, Simon[230] found only 10 (1·86 per cent) who were red-green colour-blind, and no cases of yellow-blue or of complete colour blindness. Among American Negroes, the average incidence as given by Lewis[161] is 3.75 per cent, and this writer quotes the average figure for Whites in America as 8·22 per cent, and in Europe as 7·95 per cent.

The frequency described by Simon is particularly interesting in relation to the theories of Post, as described by Coon[74]. The latter writes:

> "In 1962 R. H. Post suggested that high frequencies of colour blindness illustrate relaxed selection. . . . Another illustration is myopia. Post divided the numerous populations tested for these defects into three groups: people who still live primarily by hunting and gathering; those who have fairly recently begun to grow crops, raise domestic animals, or both; and those whose ancestors were engaged in food production for thousands of years. Among the hunters only about 2 per cent of the males are colour-blind. Among the intermediate group the toll rises to about 3·3 per cent, and in the third it varies from about 6 per cent to 10 per cent. . . . Post reasoned that hunters need accurate colour vision to succeed in the chase, or even to survive, that farmers and herdsmen are less dependent on colour vision, and urban populations are the least dependent on it."

Coon emphasizes that these differences have nothing to do with race as such, but simply imply that those peoples in any race whose ancestors gave up hunting the earliest have the highest frequency of colour blindness. The same considerations may well apply to myopia, which Gelfand[113] says is exceptionally rare in Africans.

Infectious and Malnutritional Diseases

In the interest of conciseness, these diseases have already been discussed in conjunction with the infections and dietetic deficiencies from which they arise.

Anaemias

Anaemias are exceedingly common and include, not only those seen in the temperate zone, but many others resulting from dietary deficiencies and infections that are characteristic of the tropics.

Particularly common in both sexes are iron deficiency anaemias which are usually due, not to dietary deficiency of iron, but to its excessive loss, as in hookworm infections where the infestation has been heavy and prolonged. Megaloblastic anaemias are also common in women suffering from folic acid deficiency in pregnancy.

The findings in a series of 52 patients with severe anaemia (Hb < 9g per cent), intensively studied in Kenya by Ferguson *et al.*,[93] are probably fairly representative. They found that 24 cases showed an iron deficiency anaemia (probably caused in 9 by hookworms, and in 8 by a gastro-intestinal pathology), 8 cases were megaloblastic anaemias (mostly in women and due to folic acid deficiency), 10 cases were haemolytic anaemias (of which 3 were suffering from sickle-cell disease), 5 cases showed aplastic anaemia and 3 leukaemia.

Hypertension and Atheroma

Hypertension has interest for psychiatry, not only for its psychiatric effects, but for the question of how far it is itself an outcome of psychological factors. For, as Shaper and Saxton[223] say: "The relative importance of inheritance, psychological stress, dietary factors, hormonal and electrolytic disturbances and renal ischaemia have still to be determined."

In most populations studied in Europe and North America the mean blood pressure rises steadily with age, and in the United States the prevalence of hypertension is roughly twice as great at each age level for the Negro population as for the White.

Earlier writers in East Africa observed a very different picture from this. Thus Donnison,[83] in a study of 1,000 male Africans in Kenya, found that both the systolic and diastolic mean pressures rose up to the age of 40 years and thereafter fell; while Williams,[263] in a study of 394 male Africans of Uganda, found that the mean systolic pressures remained practically stationary after 40 years while the diastolic tended to fall after 50 years.

This picture is not, or is no longer, universally true, for most writers in recent years have tended to emphasize the commonness of hypertension, as does Fraser,[102] in South Africa, and Brown,[45] in Nigeria. In fact the prevalence seems to vary considerably from one part of Africa to another, not only in terms of East, West, and South, but sometimes as between tribes in one small area as was shown by Shaper *et al.*[224] in northern Kenya. Moreover, the causation varies very much. Thus, while Fraser[102] in South Africa, and Akinkugbe[2] in Nigeria found that most of their cases were cases of essential hypertension, Hutt and Coles[131] found that most of their cases seen at autopsy were not.

The picture may indeed be changing in time. Most interesting in this context is Akinkugbe and Ojo's[3] comparison of urban and rural groups in Nigeria, where they found that the mean systolic and diastolic pressures of the former were higher than those of the latter in almost all age groups; and Monekosso's[182] reference to the recent increase of severe hypertension in the major urban centres.

Finally, cardiac infarction seems to be universally rare or absent, and severe atheroma quite uncommon. In view of the association between raised serum cholesterol and coronary heart disease, as shown by Ancel Keys *et al.*,[144] Edozien's[87] study is of great interest. He found that, compared with Europeans, the cholesterol levels were strikingly low throughout childhood in the symptom-free Nigerian children he examined, and remained low in adults of lower income group, but approached very closely to the mean value for Europeans in Nigerian adults of the professional class.

Endocrine Disease

All the major endocrine diseases described in medical text-books are to be found in Africans, but on the whole they are curiously uncommon. This applies to Addison's disease, acromegaly, Cushing's syndrome, myxoedema and Grave's disease.

Davies[77] has emphasized the importance of sex hormone disturbance secondary to cirrhosis of the liver, which is exceedingly common in Africans throughout the continent, and which may well often be due, as Davies believes, to chronic malnutrition. Among the many effects of this cirrhosis is its interference with the liver's function of inactivating oestrogens. Thus signs of oestrinization, and accordingly of feminization, are likely to be widespread.

Davies has suggested that this may explain a large number of physical attributes of Bantu Africans, such as: slender build, soft satiny skin, hairlessness, and flexible joints, the relatively common occurrence in the male of testicular atrophy, gynecomastia, and cancer of the breast. He also wrote: "It is not to be supposed that the evil effects of oestrinization or other hormonal defects induced by malnutrition are confined to the conditions briefly discussed here. Oestrin produces changes in personality and mentality which may be of the greatest importance in African life."

In general, some degree of physical feminization is common, though by no means universal, moreover, it would seem that, although some of the physical attributes indicative of feminization have a hormonal basis which is pathological on the lines described by Davies, others, such as hairlessness and flexibility, are much more likely to be part of the genetic racial pattern adaptive to life in a tropical forest region discussed in the first chapter.

Neurological Disease

The common infective conditions that are seen especially in neurological units—pyogenic, tuberculous, syphilitic, and virus encephalites—have already been discussed. They accounted for over half of a series of 700 neurological cases in a 4-year period at Ibadan and described by Kaushik.[141]

Cerebro-vascular disease used to be rare, at least in Uganda, where Muwazi and Trowell[185] saw only 2 cases (of cerebral haemorrhage) in 269 neurological cases they examined in a 2-year period ending in 1942. It is no longer rare in tropical Africa, now accounting for 16·3 per cent of Kaushik's above-mentioned series in Nigeria, and for 18·7 per cent of Ojiambo's[189] series of 75 neurological cases seen in Kenya. In Nigeria (Kaushik[141]) and in Uganda (Billinghurst[30]) research has shown that cerebral thrombosis and cerebral haemorrhage—with or without hypertension—and subarachnoid haemorrhage are all common.

Tropical neuropathies are mysterious conditions which may often be malnutritional in origin and occur throughout tropical Africa; accounting for 5·6 per cent of Kaushik's series and about 12 per cent of Ojiambo's. On the clinical side, and in Monekosso's[181] words, the syndromes are "characterized by isolated or multiple presentation of the following clinical lesions: mental symptoms, cranial nerve disturbances, spinal cord lesions, affections of spinal nerve roots and syndromes of polyneuropathy".

Cerebral tumours are not very rare and on the whole are of similar types to those seen elsewhere (see Billinghurst[29]), but tuberculomas play a larger part than in Europe (see Muwazi and Trowell[185]) and metastases of bronchial carcinoma remain uncommon.

It remains to mention that subdural haematomas are not uncommon (see Billinghurst[30]) and may present with psychiatric symptoms; idiopathic epilepsy is very common but will be discussed in a later chapter; and multiple sclerosis is rare to vanishing point, though two cases have recently been described by Foster and Harries.[101]

Alcohol and other drugs

Alcohol is widely consumed, commonly in East Africa as beer made by the fermentation of millets or, in West Africa, as palm wine. Its consumption plays an integral part in the ceremonial and other social occasions that punctuate indigenous life. Solitary drinking is probably rare.

Drunkenness is common and a cause of much crime. Thus, in a series of 100 consecutive cases of capital crime seen by the present writer in Kenya, it headed the list of causes, being the main cause in 23, and playing a conspicuous part in others. A petty quarrel at a drinking party is apt to build up to a fracas in which someone is killed, perhaps by his best friend; and the latter will excuse himself afterwards on the grounds that the drink, not himself, was wholly to blame.

Delirium tremens, though commonly seen in European men in the tropics, is hardly to be found in Africans.

Cannabis, or Indian hemp, is increasingly consumed in Lagos, where Boroffka[37] believes it is a potent cause of insanity. He found that 224 patients admitted to the Lagos mental hospital in a 4-year period gave a history of cannabis consumption, and he believed that about half of these were suffering from a toxic psychosis due to the consumption, and especially the smoking, of this drug.

Catha, or Khat, is commonly chewed for its mildly stimulating effect. If taken to excess and to the exclusion of other food, psychotic episodes may be precipitated, as has been described by the present writer.[49]

Diseases of Stress

Finally, on the subject of the "diseases of stress" in Uganda, Trowell[248] wrote in 1950:

"The following diseases are far less common in Africans: rheumatoid arthritis, psoriasis, essential hypertension, coronary–artery disease, hypertensive cerebral haemorrhage, thyrotoxicosis, and peptic ulcer. . . . Professor Selye seems to have grouped together under his title of 'diseases of the general adaptation syndrome' the large majority, but not all, of the diseases which are uncommon among Africans. This is more than a coincidence: it is a fact of overwhelming importance. Probably, however, none of these diseases is totally absent; and my clinical impression is that they are commoner among upper-class Africans, who are better fed and less exposed to certain infections."

These remarks remain as true today for some of these conditions but, for essential hypertension and for peptic ulceration, they are no longer so true, even in Uganda.

One has therefore to ask, first, whether it is possible that examples of the latter formerly existed but did not present themselves to the practitioners of European medicine (which seems most unlikely in the case of peptic ulcer at least); and, secondly, whether there has been a real change of incidence in time. Studies of incidence in different social categories of the same population are, above all, needed here, and could illuminate much more than the African scene.

PART TWO

THE PROBLEM

The
Nature-Nurture Issue

The previous chapters have dealt with the background, physical and cultural, of the African. It has been shown on the physical plane that infections or malnutrition or both are so common, particularly in childhood, as to be the rule rather than the exception. Thus, even those adults who appear to be fit must often be carrying the permanent scars of earlier illness in, for instance, the liver and spleen. And since the impact of these illnesses is commonly greatest at a time of life when the child should be developing in mind most rapidly, these scars may often be mental or even cerebral. Finally, the cultural factors were described with little consideration of their effects although, on general principles, they are bound to "suppress some developmental potentialities" in Africans, as in members of any other culture, as was mentioned earlier.

In a book designed to consider the normal (as well as the disturbed) mentality of Africans, and designed to consider this in relation to genetic and environmental factors one is therefore confronted with the problem of where this normality is to be found. Clearly, if this "normality" is to be defined in terms of a physical and cultural background that would be regarded as normal in Europe, it is not to be found in Africa. There are some rural areas where the physical factors seem by European standards to be satisfactory, but in these areas the cultural factors diverge on the lines described. In urban areas some Africans have now lost their tribal culture but, by and large, these are often exceptional people who are still seldom more than one remove, by generations, from their traditional culture. Can American evidence help? The American Negro, however, is seldom of pure Negro ancestry, and those who are relatively pure live mostly, for historical reasons, at a low economic level; so the study of these is for the present purpose also not without difficulties.

Finally therefore one has to ask two questions. First, is there any likelihood that African mentality is in any way basically different from European; and, secondly, is there any possibility of discovering that difference, if it exists?

In regard to the first question, opposing views have been expressed. In a "Statement on Race" by UNESCO in 1951 it was maintained that "Available scientific knowledge provides no basis for believing that the groups of mankind differ in their innate capacity for intellectual and emotional development". Yet it is clear that the divergent evolution of the Caucasoid and Congoid races has been sufficiently prolonged to have resulted in several striking, and genetically based, physical differences between them. It is equally clear that the great mental differences that distinguish men as individuals are partly based on genetic factors. It therefore seems to the present writer that it would be astonishing if these two races should have remained identical in the genetic basis of their mental faculties; that to imagine this would, indeed, be an affront to the ability of man as a biological species to make evolutionary use of those parts of his gene pool that underlie so much of his individual diversity, and in face of the grossly different environments he has lived in. In this belief one finds oneself in good company for, as Muller[183] says: "To the great majority of geneticists it seems absurd to suppose that psychological characteristics are subject to entirely different laws of heredity or development than other biological characteristics."

In regard to the second question posed above, one can only see, in the light of later chapters, whether an answer can be found.

PART THREE

THE BRAIN

Morphology
and the EEG

This chapter is concerned with the morphology and electro-physiology of the brain.

A variety of studies in these fields have been made, both in Africa and America but, since malnutrition, particularly in infancy, may have played a part in the African findings at least, something must first be said about this. Thereafter the adult brain, in regard to its total size, shape, fissuration, histology, and electro-encephalography will be discussed.

Malnutrition and the brain

Silvera and Jelliffe[228] observed an abnormal fatty degeneration of the liver in Nigerian infants of a few weeks old and even in the new-born, and were thus led to infer that the pathological results of malnutrition began in some cases with malnutrition of the pregnant woman. Since neurone formation occurs in the later months of pregnancy and ceases about the time of birth, this finding suggested the possibility that malnutrition in pregnancy, which is far from rare, may impinge on the foetus at the very time when its neurones are developing and thus result in an arrest of cerebral development which might be irremedial.

Stoch and Smythe[240] compared the progress of two groups of Cape Coloured children, one group having been severely under-nourished and the other adequately nourished. There were 21 children (10M, 11F) in each group; they were aged between 10 months and 3 years at the beginning of the investigation, and were examined at 6- to 12-monthly intervals for periods of 2 to 7 years. At each examination height, weight, and head circumference were measured and the intelligence (which will be discussed in a later section) was assessed. It was assumed that head circumference reflects fairly accurately the brain size and that the small error—which arises from the fact that the head circumference goes on increasing after the age of 4 years when brain growth practically ceases—should not affect the comparative sizes of the heads of children of the same ages.

It was found that at all ages the undernourished group fell below the control group in mean head circumference and that when last measured the mean difference was 0·90 inches, this being statistically significant ($t = 4·52$, $p < 0·01$). In the older children this difference was considered likely to be permanent as little increase in this dimension occurs after the age of 10 years.

Brown[47] investigated the brain weights of children coming to autopsy at Kampala, Uganda over a 12-year period from 1953 to 1964. Those children diagnosed as having malnutrition, either specified as marasmus or kwashiorkor, or as being generally under-nourished were designated as "malnourished"; while all those not so diagnosed were designated as "non-malnourished" (since some degree of sub-optimal nutrition might be present in many if not most children dying in the hospital).

A break-down of 200 of these children for each of the first five years of life can be expressed in tabular form.

Age	Non-malnourished No.	Mean Weight	Malnourished No.	Mean Weight	Significance of difference
Less than 1 year	29	620 g	12	547 g	Not significant
1–2 years	23	905 g	39	800 g	P < 0·01
2–3 years	25	1,050 g	29	888 g	P < 0·01
3–4 years	18	1,068 g	9	961 g	P < 0·05
4–5 years	9	1,127 g	7	985 g	P < 0·05

The children in this series who died of kwashiorkor were often described as having oedema and congestion of the brain and, if it had been possible to allow for this, the differences in weight would often have been even greater.

Brown writes that: "The implication of these findings is that the adverse influence of undernutrition on brain growth may be present at a critical period very early in life." Since the period of major brain growth is from about the fifth foetal month till the end of the first year after birth, it may well be that malnutrition at this time limits the full potential for brain development in those affected.

Total size

Since it is probable, as Simmons[229] observed, that attempts to compare two series of brain weights or brain capacities are rather valueless unless both series (in this case Whites and Negroes) are assessed by the same technique and preferably by the same person, only those studies that seem to have fulfilled these criteria will be referred to here.

Todd, as quoted by Cobb,[61] published data on cranial capacity based on 198 Whites (167M, 31F) and 104 Negroes (87M, 17F). The Whites had mean capacities of 1,391 cc (M) and 1,232 cc (F) respectively; the Negroes of 1,350 cc (M) and 1,221 cc (F) respectively; and the proportion of the latter to the former for both sexes was thus 97·4 per cent.

Pearl[199] published data on brain weights based on 403 autopsies made by I. Russell on White, Mixed, and Negro men who died in the American Civil War. The mean brain weight of the 24 Whites was 1,470·6 g; and of the 139 Negroes was 1,354·8 g; the weight of the latter being 92·1 per cent of the former.

Simmons[229] published data on cranial capacity based on 1,361 White (1,179M, 182F) and 880 Negro skulls (661M, 219F). The Whites had mean capacities of 1,517·5 cc (M) and 1,338·8 cc (F) respectively; the Negroes of 1,467·1 cc (M) and 1,310·9 cc (F) respectively; and the proportion of the latter to the former for both sexes was thus about 97 per cent.

Connolly[72] published weights of 60 White brains (50M, 10F) mostly German, and of 45 Negro (36M, 9F) mostly American. The Whites had mean weights of 1,288 g (M) and 1,226 g (F) respectively; the Negroes of 1,198 g (M) and 1,127 g (F) respectively; and the proportion of the Negro to the White series for both sexes was thus 92·9 per cent.

Thus although the proportions vary considerably in different studies—from 92·1 per cent to 97·4 per cent in this series—they do seem to point in one direction and the position can perhaps hardly be better expressed than it was by Cobb[62] when he said: "Summation of available data on brain weight suggests that the average brain of the Negro who comes to the dissecting or necropsy table is slightly smaller than that of the fairly comparable White, as indicated by studies of weight direct and of cranial capacity."

The significance of this finding for psychology is, however, very indirect. In regard to brains in general, their weight is related to total body-weight and there is, for instance, no difference in the average intelligence of European men and women, although the latter's brain capacity is, on average, only nine-tenths that of the former. Gross divergencies from the mean in any race are often associated with mental defect; but, within the normal range, the positive correlation of intelligence and head size is rather small, being of the order of $+ 0·1$ to $+ 0·2$, according to figures published by Penrose.[202]

General shape

As in the case of brain size, differences in shape are statistical, never absolute. The Negro brain, both in Africa and America, and according to many writers (e.g. Bianchi,[19] Bork-Feltkamp,[36] Connolly,[72] Gordon,[118] Simmons,[229] and Vint[254] is relatively long and narrow as compared with the European mean; and the cranial index (which approximates to 75 in many estimates) thus often becomes the variable showing the most significant racial difference. Thus in Simmons' previously mentioned series the mean lengths of the Negro brains were greater than those of the Whites by 3·2 per cent and 3·5 per cent in the males and females respectively; the mean breadths of the White brains were greater than those of the Negroes by 4·3 per cent and 3·5 per cent in the males and females respectively; and the cranial index was 74·3 (M) and 74·9 (F) in the Negroes and 79·7 (M) and 80·3 (F) in the Whites.

Several writers have commented on low height as characteristic of Negro brains. Bork-Feltkamp[36] has done so; Todd, as quoted by Cobb,[61] found that variations in brain volume were mainly and directly related to variations in the height dimension; and Vint[254] said: "The reduction in size of the native brain, as compared with the European, seems to be accounted for mainly by a failure in the development of height". In Simmons'[229] series, however, the White advantage in this respect was only about 1 per cent.

Bean,[17] reported that the frontal lobes were smaller on average in Negroes than in Whites and that there was a greater number of large frontal lobes among the Caucasian brains he examined (66 large, 22 small) and a greater number of small frontal lobes among the Negro brains (106 small, 59 large). According to Connolly[72] the frontal and occipital regions occupy a slightly smaller proportion of the brain, and the parietal region a slightly greater in the Negro, but it has to be said that his assessments are based on certain anatomical delineations which are valuable for descriptive purposes but have limited meaning in regard to function.

In general, indeed, although the brain shape of the Negro is somewhat characteristic, the data in regard to shape are such as can throw little light on function.

Fissuration

The outstanding work on the fissuration, or pattern of surface grooving, of the Negro brain is that by Connolly.[72] Admittedly the number of brains was limited—30 Negro being compared with 30 White—but a larger survey could hardly have been made without some sacrifice of the meticulous precision which characterizes this eminent monograph. The White brains were of Germans from Berlin, while the Negro brains derived from 28 American Negroes (regarded as full-blooded Negroes according to anthropological tests applied by Hrdlicka) and 2 Zulus. 4 of the Whites and 5 of the Negroes were females.

Connolly found that no morphological features were exclusively characteristic of either the White or the Negro brain, but that various features occurred with different frequencies in these two populations. Among a great multiplicity of details, perhaps his most interesting observation from the point of view of the present monograph was the existence of a greater degree of fissuration and of anastomosis between the fissures in the Whites. Connolly observes that these features show some positive correlation with brain size, and that the White brains were, on the average, larger than the Negro brains; but he evidently considers that the fissural difference is not wholly accounted for on these grounds. The form of the sulci was probably also related in some measure to the general difference in brain shape. Bork-Feltkamp,[36] in an earlier study of 6 African brains, observed a predominantly longitudinal direction of the fissures which he related to the elongated brain.

Some observers have attached importance to exposure of the insula—a common finding in the Negro—but according to Connolly, "It is probable that the differences in frequencies (of various forms of the anterior limbs of the lateral fissure) is due to the shape of the brain in the two races, the White (German) brain being shorter than that of the Negro. This would tend to offer resistance to the downward growth of the frontal operculum and bring the orbital and parieto-frontal opercula together, thus more frequently covering the insula."

In general, the study of sulcal patterns, in the present state of knowledge of brain function, is of limited value for psychology. Mental capacity is surely related in part to the extent of cortical surface, and clearly complexity of fissuration gives some evidence of this extent. But this evidence is too dependent on subjective estimates. Moreover it is only approximate, for it ignores the sulcal depth. It is known for instance that certain groups of prehistoric men, such as the Neanderthals, had larger mean cranial capacities than have most modern European populations; and it is open to speculation, since fossil evidence gives no clue to sulcal depth, that economy of cerebral volume may have followed on the heels of overgrowth, and that a small but deeply fissured brain might be an upward step. However this may be, in the absence of an objective method of assessment of total cortical surface area, estimates of total fissuration can throw little light on psychology.

Cortical histology

In regard to the histology of the African brain, Vints'[253],[254] work, published in two short articles, stands by itself.

The fields of study were slightly different in the two articles in that the former was based on samples from the prefrontal cortex of 35 brains whereas, in the latter, samples were examined from 8 cortical areas in the several lobes of 100 brains. The latter study, however, includes the material gathered in the former, and the two articles lend themselves to summarizing as a whole.

The brains were collected in Kenya and were those of male adults who had died in the native hospitals of Nairobi, but not in the mental or prison hospitals. The brains were fresh and appeared to be normal. Apart from these criteria there was no selection. The subjects were all Negro, mostly Bantu, and had been mainly if not entirely without formal education of European type.

Vint measured the thickness of the several laminae of the cortex and compared the averages for each of the 8 areas with those given for the corresponding areas of European brains as measured by Von Economo. His findings can be expressed as follows:

Laminae	Percentage difference as compared with Europeans
L. zonalis	+9
L. supragranularis	−16
L. granularis int	−17
L. infragranularis	−8
Total cortex	−15

The figures for each area correspond fairly closely to the above average figures for the laminae as a whole, except that the infragranular layer in the area striata showed a figure of + 14 per cent.

Vint reminded his readers that the supragranular layer is the last to be evolved, and pointed out that in his Africans it attained to only 84 per cent of European development, and that the difference (of 15 per cent) in total cortical thickness was mainly accounted for by the narrowness of this lamina. He stated that "for the whole brain the average ratio of the supragranular layer to the infragranular layer is 5:8. The average ratio of the figures of Von Economo for the same areas is 6:8."

In regard to the cortical neurones, Vint[254] says: "Cell counts carried out on sections from the different portions of the brains examined failed to show a diminution in the number per unit area, as compared with the brain of the European. Any apparent reduction assumed from inspection of photographs is attributable to the cells being smaller in the native brain, and by the fact that many of the cells are only slightly differentiated.... Cell counts per unit area are the same in the African and European brains." Vint drew attention to the facts that increase in cortical thickness after birth (in Europeans) is due almost entirely to the conversion of neuroblasts into adult neurones, mainly in the supragranular layer, and that post-natal increase in the weight and size of the brain as a whole is due mainly to myelination of the nerve axons from the neurones of the supragranular layer in association areas, since other neurones become mature and their axons become myelinated mainly before birth. Vint concluded his first article with the words: "Thus from both the average weight of the native brain and from measurements of its pre-frontal cortex I have arrived, in this preliminary investigation, at the conclusion that the stage of cerebral development reached by the average native is that of the average European boy of between 7 and 8 years of age." He emphasized, however, in regard to the undifferentiated cells (which also occur but in smaller numbers in Europeans) that it was 'impossible to say how many would mature under conditions of life and education different to those which normally obtain today'."

Vint's work has been criticized on various grounds, perhaps most importantly on the grounds that the subjects were likely to have been chronically unfit in life. Vint himself has shown elsewhere that about 70 per cent of the African subjects who came to autopsy at Nairobi were suffering from cirrhosis of the liver (to mention but one common African abnormality) and these were not excluded. Moreover, the brains that were studied formed part of a series of 389 brains which Vint[254] had assessed as having a mean weight only 89·4 per cent of that of European brains—a figure which is so far below those found by others that it might suggest that the subjects had been suffering from chronic malnutrition.

However, if Vint had waited for an adequate series of subjects whose health had conformed to European standards, he would be waiting yet; a point which was mentioned in the previous chapter and which may indeed be a significant part of his very valuable study.

Electro-encephalography

Interest in the EEG patterns of Africans, as compared with Europeans, was initiated by French workers—Gallais and three others[104, 105]—who examined 100 apparently normal African soldiers from several parts of West Africa. They compared their findings with those of Gibbs who, in a study of 3,000 apparently normal European subjects, regarded 13·8 per cent of these as electro-encephalographically abnormal by criteria which Gallais *et al.* also applied to their own data. By these standards they found 58 per cent of the African subjects' records were abnormal.

These studies were followed in 1953 by that of Mundy-Castle and two others[184] in South Africa. This study dealt with 138 apparently normal adults of whom 66 were Bantu Africans and 72 were Europeans, and the 2 groups were compared. Although in this study there were several minor differences of statistical significance between the 2 groups, no significant differences in the incidence of abnormality or questionable normality were observed. Among the minor differences, however, there were two that agreed with differences observed by Gallais *et al.*, for both groups of observers recorded a high incidence of little or no response to flicker, and a different cortical distribution of alpha rhythm suggestive of a more anterior origin of this activity among Africans.

In 1956 Verhaegen[252], in a study of 74 men whom he had selected as being a representative sample of the Congolese population, found the proportion of these who showed EEG abnormalities was no higher than that found in Europeans; while in 1957 Merrill and Cook[179] compared the results of their EEG examination of 279 White and 117 Negro adults in the United States, and found no significant differences between these groups.

In 1959 and 1963 Nelson, as recorded by Biesheuvel,[28] in studies of children who had survived kwashiorkor or were mildly affected by it, found that the evolution of the faster EEG rhythms was significantly retarded, that this was only partially redressed during recovery, and that in more than one-third of the subjects there were focal disturbances in the temporal lobes.

In 1965 Pampiglione[195] investigated the EEGs of children living in the Greater London area and whose ages ranged from 5 months to 3 years. 17 of the children were of African Negro origin and 23 were of European (19) or Indian (4) origin. They had been selected from a larger group and were those in whom no gross brain disorder was likely to be present. EEG studies were made up to 6 times in each child over periods of 6–10 months from the first test. He found that a well-formed sinusoidal rhythmic activity at about 5–6 c/s in the occipital region was observed after eye-closure in the Negro children by the age of 5–7 months, whereas in most European children it was not seen in this frequency range before the age of 9 months. Furthermore, while in both European and Indian children a definite alpha rhythm at 8–9 c/s did not appear until the age of 24–28 months, in most African Negro children this maturational change was already present by the age of about 18–24 months. He wrote: "It therefore seems probable, from the observations made on this group of children, that some individual differences in the rate of EEG development might be related, among other possibilities, to an ethnical or genetic factor which affects cerebral maturation in a way yet to be understood."

In sum, therefore, it would seem that the grosser abnormalities observed by Gallais and his colleagues were probably related to organic cerebral disturbance (sicklaemia, malnutrition, or infectious disease) as was indeed envisaged as a possibility by these writers, but that differences of alpha rhythm which may be biological occur within the normal range; while Pampiglione's findings are of considerable interest since they clearly accord with those of Geber and Dean, whose studies of the psycho-motor development of African infants will be described in the chapter on *Psychology*.

PART FOUR

THE MIND

Psychology

Classical conceptions

Many attempts have been made to describe African mentality but, in recent years at least, usually with the reservation that these were classical conceptions, popular stereotypes, etc. These descriptions, however, are by no means false. They represent a facet of the truth and, as such, must be recorded.

Their meaning is quite another story, as will appear later; and it should be said forthwith that a part of this meaning has been well expressed by Bateson[14] when writing on the rather different subject of Pidgin English. He said:

"It is, like the rudimentary culture which develops between passengers on a ship, a rather gay, rather irresponsible and meaningless world. Both White man and Native have put aside many of the fundamentals of life. The indentured native has left his kin behind in the village and is embarked on an adventure which he knows will one day end ... for the time being he is suspended in an interim period of life ... and the complexities and responsibilities of his normal background are in abeyance."

What has been said?

Westermann[259] is well worth quoting at some length. He wrote:

"With the Negro emotional, momentary and explosive thinking predominates ... dependence on excitement, on external influences and stimuli, is a characteristic sign of primitive mentality. Primitive man's energy is unstable and spasmodic. He is easily fired with enthusiasm for an undertaking and begins his work with great zest; but his interest dies down quickly and the work is abandoned ... Where the stimulus of emotion is lacking the Negro shows little spontaneity and is passive. He waits for what is coming to him and evades what is inconvenient, or adapts himself to it, instead of bravely confronting the obstacles of life and mastering them. ... The Negro has but few gifts for work which aims at a distant goal and requires tenacity, independence, and foresight.

"The interest which the African takes in things is not an academic one. They concern him in so far as they are useful to him or can do him harm ... observation is often superficial; conclusions have been drawn from it in a most uncritical way; and instead of further thought on the matter, word spinning has seemed sufficient ... knowledge mixed with a child-like play of the imagination.

"A man does not plan, set himself an aim and exercise his strength in attaining it. The individual as such has no aim in life if his task is to become exactly like the rest.... The motives for his actions are predominantly social, not individual, and are deeply influenced by public opinion.... Personal responsibility is avoided wherever possible."

The French neuropsychiatrists Gallais and Planques[106] recorded as classical notions of the African, with particular reference to the population of the then French possessions in central and west Africa, that

"The best known traits of the normal psychology of the African are, above all, the importance of physical needs (nutrition, sexuality); and a liveliness of the emotions which is counter-balanced by their poor duration. Sensations and movements comprise the chief part of his existence. Intellectual life, evocation of the past, and projects for the future preoccupy him but little. Separated from these regulating influences, he lives essentially in the present (in this sense like a child), and his conduct submits to influences and impulses of the passing moment and thus appears 'explosive and chaotic' as Spencer says ...

"Characteristic of this emotional lability are such facts as the following which each of us has witnessed many times in Africa. Two Africans have engaged in argument (an unrepaid loan, an unfaithful wife, an uncompleted bride price, a stolen kid, etc.). Beginning with bargaining, the discussion merely animated, becomes vehement, the tone rises, insults and abuse are exchanged in Homeric fashion, shouting is accompanied by frenzied gesticulation and staring eyes, and at the summit of their fury the two are about to come to blows. In a few moments a ferocious battle will begin. If at that moment someone makes a joke, the fury is instantly dissipated in an immense roar of laughter, the appearance of anger gives place to that of exuberant mirth, and our two antagonists comment merrily on the jest which has produced this surprising volte face, giving each other great thumps on the back and calling the bystanders to witness the full flavour of the joke."

Another French writer, Barbé[13] summarized current stereotypes on African mentality thus:

"(1) Priority of functions closely related to physiological activity, especially sensory, whence derives a superiority of concrete memory, ability to acquire vocabularies and the niceties of grammar, verbal fecundity and a pronounced taste for conversation.

"(2) From the affective point of view, impulsivity violent but unsustained, inconstancy, recklessness—to borrow a word from modern characterologies, an 'immaturity' ('primarity') which prevents complexity and integration in the emotional life.

"(3) In the field of intelligence, an inaptitude for that which appears to be its essential function: co-ordinating the parts of a whole, perceiving abstract relations particularly mathematical.

"(4) At the level of action, sociability, love of routine, lack of persistent effort, passive obedience to events. In general, a submission of integrative and creative power to the profit of automatisms and instincts."

Williams,[264] writing about Africans of the Gold Coast, said:

"Compared with the white races he seems to lack initiative and constructive ideas, although he may be a shrewd judge of the attainments of others. He has a childlike gift for distinguishing the sincere from the false, the shepherd from the hireling. He is almost invariably dishonest. He wishes to attain wealth without expending too much energy. He does not consider there is any obligation to honesty beyond the members of his own family. For them he will give up anything he has and steal anything he has not. Outsiders are fair game and are treated with the utmost callousness. He is conventional and loves talking. He will invent all manner of fabricated excuses out of politeness combined with a facile verbosity. Power of observation is astonishingly defective . . . They seem to be incapable of sustained effort . . . An African has little imagination and little humility. His self-esteem is often ludicrous. And yet he is willing to shelter behind 'You can't expect better from a poor African' . . . I have seen enough of the excellent qualities of the Africans—their good nature and cheerfulness, their astuteness, their uncomplaining fidelity, their patience in very great trials— to know that they are worth educating. The qualities most in need of education are observation, imagination and judgement."

Finally, it is worth quoting a few words from the editorial of the *East African Medical Journal* of May 1960 which ran as follows: "There is one aspect of African life which so far as we know has never been explained. Why is it that the bright-eyed merry-hearted lively little African child up to about the age of 7 or 8 years, thereafter undergoes a subtle change into a much more listless, if not actually apathetic, adolescent?"

These are the common European conceptions of the African. Examples could be multiplied indefinitely, but it would be a pointless pastime, for these are representative; and it is clear that, as African life impinges on European observers, these conceptions are very often just. However completely they may be explained away, these attributes are not only apparent to most Europeans in Africa, but often bedevil relations with the latter. They are therefore worth summarizing.

The African accordingly has been described as conventional; highly dependent on physical and emotional stimulation; lacking in foresight, tenacity, judgement and humility; inapt for sound abstraction and for logic; given to phantasy and fabrication; and, in general, as unstable, impulsive, unreliable, irresponsible, and living in the present without reflection or ambition, or regard for the rights of people outside his own circle. To counteract these ruderies, he has also been described as cheerful, stoical, self-confident, sociable, loyal, emotionally intuitive, and eloquent, and as bearing no grudges and having an excellent memory, a large vocabulary, and an aptitude for music and the dance.

Psychological Assessments

(a) *Infancy and early childhood*

Geber and Dean[109] in the course of a study in Uganda of the psychological changes accompanying kwashiorkor, and needing to establish norms of psycho-motor development for African children, examined their development within the first 8 days from birth.

They examined 107 African infants (52 boys and 55 girls) by a detailed technique as used by André Thomas and his collaborators. All the babies and their mothers were without any known disease. Most were Bantu while others were Nilotic or Hamitic, but no difference between these groups could be distinguished. The writers found that "there seemed to be no doubt that these

African children had been born at a more advanced stage of development, judged by the method used, than the normal European child. The results of the examination were so consistent, and the degree of advance was so great, that there was little room for uncertainty. Much of the activity corresponded to an age of 4–6 weeks. Some was even more precocious" and such as "might be expected at 6–8 weeks".

For comparison with these infants, Geber and Dean also examined 15 European and 60 Indian infants born about the same time in Uganda and found that "The European children gave exactly the results that have been found in Europe, and the Indian children gave almost similar results. Neither group showed any great degree of overlap with the African children."

These authors[110] later studied over 300 African children in Uganda from the first few weeks of life to 6 years old, and who had been reared in the traditional way. They found that their "developmental quotient", though much higher than that of European infants at first, gradually approached the European mean until, by about two years old, their quotients were about the same and then remained so for the other four years studied.

They also examined 60 African children from Westernized (évolués) homes, where the parents were sophisticated on European lines, where infant care followed these lines (infants in cots, feeding at set times, etc.) and where the homes contained all the appurtenances found in European homes (furniture, toys, books, radio, etc.). They found that the developmental quotient of these children up to the age of 2 years, though precocious by European standards, was not so advanced as that of the rural infants, but that after that age this precocity was well maintained for the remaining 4 years studied.

They inferred from all these data that the maintenance of the new-born precocity for the first 2 years was partly related to the traditional patterns of infant care (encouraging neck muscle control, and stimulating general bodily movements and mental interest), and that the loss of this precocity after 2 years was related to a gross lack of mental stimulation in the African rural home for children above that age.

Faladé[91] investigated the psycho-motor development of more than 100 African infants in Senegal. Using Gesell's techniques she found that, throughout the period extending from birth to 15 months there was a marked precocity in infantile development, notably in the acquisition of manual prehension and of the sitting position. Thereafter, this precocity was not maintained and Faladé related this first to the fact that the mothers, not wanting the breast-feeding period to end, actually discouraged independence in their children, and secondly to the fact that a period of apathy followed the traumatic weaning which is the rule in Senegal.

Biesheuvel[26] described a study in which data based on the psycho-motor testing of a series of healthy African babies in South Africa at monthly intervals for the first 6 months of life were compared with data obtained in an identical way for a series of Belgian babies. The findings did not confirm the total precocity of African infants observed by the earlier writers, but did demonstrate a precocity in some directions for the White and in other directions for the African infants. Thus, in following with the eyes a red ring moved in a circle before the baby's face, the Belgian infants were more advanced at all age levels; whereas in spontaneous grasping of the ring, in manipulating a rattle, and in inspecting rings and rattles when these were placed in the infant's hands the African babies were more advanced than the White up to the age of 4 months but fell behind in the 5th and 6th months.

Thus, although these psycho-motor findings on the whole are rather contradictory, it is clear that differences exist and, in view of the very early age at which they were observed, a genetic component may well be operative.

(b) *Children and adults*

General intelligence

Many attempts have been made to assess general intelligence by tests in Africans and to compare the results with those obtained in African Whites. The most prominent of these will now be described in chronological order, since this order is very relevant to the findings. Their significance or lack of significance, and the general issues involved, will be discussed thereafter.

1. Fick(1929)[94] tested 293 Zulu schoolchildren between the ages of 10 and 14 years inclusive, using the American Army Beta Test—a group test devised for the assessment of non-English-speaking recruits to the American Army. He compared the results with those obtained from 10,000 White South

African children (on whom this test had previously been standardized), and from groups of poor-White, Coloured, and Indian schoolchildren. He found that the African medians were considerably lower than those of any of the other groups, and that an average of only 1·2 per cent reached or exceeded the medians of similar ages of White children. He stressed, however, that, in regard to the African children, their education was inferior, pictures and diagrams as used in the test were strange for them, the group test situation was itself strange, their ages were doubtful and that, in general, the European tests might not be fair to them.

2. Oliver (1932)[190] performed intelligence tests on 124 European schoolboys and 93 African schoolboys, both groups in Kenya Colony. The average age of the European boys was 15 years and of the African, $19\frac{1}{2}$ years; assuming that adult mental age is reached at 15 years, 43·5 per cent of the former and 99 per cent of the latter were of full adult intelligence. He used a battery of non-verbal group tests comprising problems dealing with pictures, numbers, letters, and other symbols. He found that the African mean was 85 per cent of the European mean and that only 14 per cent of the Africans reached or exceeded the European mean. He admitted that the quality of the schooling, and familiarity with visual symbols, with pencil and paper, with the need for speed, and with the test situation itself were all in favour of the European group, and that the sampling was not ideal, but summarized these aspects in the following words: "the samples of the races tested were far from being identical apart from race, yet were probably as nearly comparable as could at present be obtained; while the tests used were probably fairer to both groups than any others available". This summary, the present writer, who is familiar with the background of the groups concerned, considers to be a fair one.

3. Fick (1939)[95] in a further study of the educability of African children in South Africa arrived at the following main conclusions.

"(a) A survey of the existing work on the educability of Natives reveals a paucity of experimental and objective data.

(b) The unanimity of these data compensates for their fewness. Around the ages of 13 and 14 Native children are from 4 to 5 years inferior to European children in educability as gauged by the results of intelligence tests.

(c) Additional data presented in the present study and based on a variety of tests and on a considerable number of cases confirm previous findings.

(d) Although all the facts regarding the educability of the Native may not be in, the available objective data point to a marked inferiority on the part of the Native in comparison with Europeans. This inferiority occurring in certain tests in which learning or environmental conditions are equalized for the Native and European groups does not appear to be of a temporary nature."

4. Biesheuvel (1943)[20] in a monograph on the subject of African intelligence, set out (a) to discover to what extent the growth of intelligence can be determined by factors other than hereditary, i.e. by cultural, home, school, nutritional, and temperamental factors; (b) to study the situation of the South African population in regard to each of these factors; and (c) to assess the validity of Professor Fick's data and interpretations in the light of these findings. He proceeded to show that intelligence can surely be influenced by all the factors mentioned, and that the total decrement from these factors in the African might well be 30 points of I.Q. He concluded that African and European intelligence cannot really be compared in South Africa but that, if one insists on doing so, one should add 30 points to African I.Q.s to allow for these factors and that, if one does this, the retardation described by Fick is entirely accounted for.

Perhaps the most important part of Biesheuvel's conclusions was simply that African and European intelligence cannot really be compared in South Africa. It would probably be as true to say that they cannot really be compared in this sort of quantitative way in any part of Africa.

Intelligence, as defined by Thouless,[244] is the "capacity for varying behaviour to meet the requirements of a changing environment". Whether this capacity is based on one general factor ("g") which underlies the entirety of a man's adaptive behaviour, or on a number of distinct factors each of which underlies capacity in some particular field (mathematics, memory, language, etc.), or on some combination of both of these principles is open to dispute. What is not in dispute is that intelligence tests, based on a large variety of tests designed to tap abilities in several fields, and resulting in a figure related to the mean achievement on these tests (the intelligence quotient or I.Q.) has been found to be of the greatest practical and predictive use for educational and other purposes in Europeans. Moreover, it is surely undeniable that the greater the similarity of the environmental background of the tested subjects, the more accurately does this figure become a measure of innate potential. The converse is equally true, however, and gives rise to the question whether a measure of this sort can have any value for the comparison of peoples whose environmental backgrounds (infective, nutritional, and cultural) are as dissimilar as those of Africans and Whites in Africa.

Most of the best tests of general intelligence in Europeans are highly dependent on a familiarity with visual symbols which is not to be found in rural Africans; while performance tests (which are sometimes fairer for the latter) are largely measures of specific abilities rather than of general intelligence. Intelligence tests, in fact, and in the words of Anastasi and Foley,[5] "Measure certain abilities required for success in the particular culture in which they were developed". Their usefulness as a measure of the overall ability of Africans in the Old World is, accordingly, a very limited one. How far this is also true for Negroes in the New World is quite another story, and will be considered in a later chapter.

Finally, and perhaps most importantly, if basic mental differences between races do exist, they may well be qualitative rather than quantitative and, on this issue, assessments of general intelligence (or I.Q. figures) give one little help. Indeed one cannot conclude this section more profitably than by quoting Biesheuvel[21] again. He wrote:

"The usefulness of 'g' was established chiefly in relation to the measurement of scholastic educability, where its level was generally rendered in the form of an I.Q. Other indices had to be used to predict occupational success and to diagnose potential talents. The I.Q., however, overshadowed these indices in the importance which was attached to it as providing an evaluation of the intellectual worth of man. When dealing with the abilities of races we cannot confine ourselves to those aspects of mental function and behaviour which happen to be rated highly in Western culture. Consequently studies which yield a profile of abilities rather than

an index of the hypothetical power of the mind are to be
preferred."

Aptitudes

To turn from the problem of general intelligence to that of
particular abilities, Biesheuvel[21] conducted an investigation of
African and European schoolchildren in Johannesburg aged
between 12 and 15 years, there being 125 subjects in each group.
The two groups were matched for age and sex and, as far as
practicable, for general intelligence and socio-economic status.
The effective educational status of the African children was inferior by about 3 years of schooling, but any attempt to match for
this would have upset the matching for age or for general intelligence in the circumstances of education in South Africa. The
tests used were Koh's Blocks, Cube Construction, Alexander
Passalong, Porteus Maze, and a Match Test which was a performance version of tests like number series and figure classification.
No significant difference was found between the means on the
Passalong, Maze and Match tests (the critical ratios being about 0·4
for these), but for the Koh's Blocks and Cube Construction tests
the African means were significantly lower than the European (the
critical ratio for these being about 3·4).

Maistriaux,[166] in a study of Congolese Africans of several age
and educational levels on a type of Cube Construction test, also
found that the mean achievements were markedly inferior to
those of Whites.

In a thematic apperception test study made by Hudson and
described by Biesheuvel,[26] a series of pictures in which the same
scene (an African hunter raising a spear, in readiness to throw it at
a buck facing him in the same plane, and in the distance between
the two, an elephant standing under a tree on a hill) was presented,
with the successive addition of depth cues to suggest perspective.
Responses were obtained from Black and White schoolchildren
and adults of many educational levels. It was found that, although
the 3-dimensional perception of both Black and White subjects
increased with age and education, the former lagged consistently
behind at all educational levels. Biesheuvel expressed the view,
both in regard to this test and to the block and cube tests, that
although the findings may suggest a genetic inferiority to manipulate and to perceive spatial relations, particularly in three
dimensions, they may also suggest that a lack of early familiarity

with pictures, building blocks, etc., can never wholly be redressed in later life.

Bourdel,[40] in a study of the Oubangien people of the Sudan, found that subjects who were classed among the poorest in all the tests (and who lay in the 8th decile) showed similar achievements to those of average Europeans (i.e. of the 5th decile) in tests of long-term verbal memory. In tests of immediate memory the advantage lay still more markedly with the Oubangiens. In regard to the general level of concentrated attention the reverse held good, and Oubangiens of high achievement in all the tests (of the 2nd decile) scarcely attained the level of average Europeans. He found in general that the best Oubangiens on each test attained the same levels as the best Europeans (metropolitan French), but that below this élite, who comprised some 6 per cent of the total tested, achievement fell rapidly away to the general mediocre and low level of the bulk of the subjects.

Although not tested and hardly amenable to testing, no study of African abilities would be complete without a reference to musical ability. Music for Africans is something more than a part of the perceptual world, it is a part of life itself, a means of communication, and something that calls for active participation. As a creative talent it is not limited to the few, and there must be few social, or even working, occasions when someone present is not prepared to extemporize, vocally or instrumentally, and when everyone else is not prepared to join in. Tracey,[246] a leading authority on African music, says: "There are hundreds of important musicians still composing indigenous music up and down the length and breadth of Africa and most of them quite unrecognized except by those native people in their own district. What is more, they are producing music which can be sung naturally by their own people, in its most effective social context."

* * *

Some further comments are called for, first, as to the lack of facility in Africans for dealing with spatial relations in 3-dimensions. No doubt this is partly due to a lack of familiarity with problems entailing this sort of understanding in early life, as hypothesized by Biesheuvel; but the present writer finds it difficult to see, on a purely environmental hypothesis, why facility in tests of this sort should be so inferior to that for such 2-dimensional tests as the Maze and the Passalong, which provide problems that are no more familiar to African children, unless some constitutional factor were also involved.

Bourdel's observation in regard to the Oubangien élite is also interesting for, although this sort of experience in tests of Africans has not often been recounted, it has often been observed in real life situations. It gives rise to a question as to whether the intellectual distribution curve in at least some African groups might be a bi-modal one, and indicative that those groups had two recent origins which had not yet thoroughly merged.

However this may be, it is not very rare to meet Africans whose intellect or character or both are of a high order by any standard, and Bourdel's observation can serve as a timely reminder that assessment of means does not tell the whole story, nor even at times the most important part of it.

Temperament

Temperamental factors have so far proved much less amenable to testing than have intellectual. Consideration of the former is therefore much more dependent on subjective assessments and, accordingly, on the views of those best qualified to develop them. This section (like the last one) therefore leans heavily on the work and thought of Dr Simon Biesheuvel, who was for many years the very distinguished Director of the South African National Institute for Personnel Research.

As was shown in Chapter 3, physiological adaptation to humid heat seems not to be greater in Africans than Whites. Biesheuvel[27] has, however, put forward the hypothesis that, by a process of natural selection, adaptation of a more psychological kind has occurred, involving temperament rather than the bodily heat—regulating mechanisms. Since activity generates heat and leads to discomfort if it is not quickly dissipated, prolonged sojourn in the tropics induces a slower, more relaxed tempo of movement, as has been shown for White settlers in Queensland. In Africans a more fundamental constitutional change may have occurred because of a higher survival rate among less active individuals.

Biesheuvel follows Heymans in believing that "activity" is a well-defined temperament variable, which may well have constitutional origins. People with a high activity level have a greater capacity for sustained effort, and more readily engage in spontaneous activity largely for its own sake than do the temperamentally inactive. In tropical Africa the former more frequently incur a variety of risks, not only in the directly physical field, but from the fact that their restless enquiring mentality is more likely to lead them into conflict with their group in societies which insist on conformity. This kind of temperament, if based on genetic factors, would therefore tend to be eliminated progressively from racial groups subjected to this sort of climate and to the sort of culture that has developed in that climate.

Personality

Since a man's total personality is the outcome of the environmental, and particularly the cultural, factors working upon his innate needs and faculties, there is no need to discuss it further in this section since this is what the rest of this chapter is about.

It is however, important to stress that people vary, as free individuals, in personality, in African as in other societies, but that they do so within a range of acceptability that is characteristic of each society; and that one is dealing in this volume with what is best described as a "modal" personality which lies within this range as it is culturally conditioned in Africa.

Environmental Effects

Psychological development, both in individuals and in human groups, is in large part the outcome of environmental factors. It cannot be studied in isolation from these. It will therefore be the concern of the rest of this chapter to consider the psychology of man in Africa in relation to these factors.

Psychology in relation to Geography and Climate

These two factors have effects which are indirect, by providing the background for the infective and nutritional factors which are discussed in the next section. They also have direct effects which are long-term and some are more immediate.

As regards the long-term effects, the possible influence of the tropical climate on the evolution of a characteristic temperament has just been discussed; while the effect of a forest environment in governing the mode of perceptual attention adumbrated in

Chapter 3, is so interwoven with the cultural influences that its full consideration must be deferred to the end of this chapter.

The short-term effects are therefore to be considered here.

Highly characteristic is a monotony of scene and a vastness which is hardly to be found in western Europe and, whether it be the open immensity of the East or South or the forest country of the West, a march of many days may result in little change of scene.

The countryside is in many ways essentially inimical to man. Apart from snakes and larger predators, there are a host of creatures that menace one's comfort (ants, bees, scorpions, midges etc), one's home (white ants), or one's crops (locusts, elephants), or did so until recently.

Particularly in the Bantu lands, African economy and the rhythm of life are closely identified with the coming of the seasonal rains. Their delay gives rise to an anxiety which is met by every means that indigenous imagination can devise; their failure (relative or complete) can be an unmitigated disaster and too often, when the rains do come, they fall in deluges which rapidly carry the parched earth to the rivers.

These are some of the adverse circumstances. Their direct psychological effects are hard to demonstrate. Yet they cannot be ignored, and it is fair to surmise that they must give rise to an abiding sense of insecurity and personal insignificance which can only be mitigated by cultural techniques which take account of them.

Psychology in relation to physical disease and malnutrition

Tropical diseases, in so far as they have anything in common with each other, result in states of chronic debility and anaemia which are, in many ways, similar in effect to malnutrition. Indeed, as in the case of infestation with various worms, of feverish illnesses, and of cirrhosis of the liver, their own effects are partly malnutritional. In so far as their effects are peculiar to themselves and are not general, their study is more suitably deferred to the chapter on psychiatry.

Malnutrition, in the form of kwashiorkor, is seen most often between the ages of 2 and 4 years. But it is now clear that this disease is always a sign of something deeper and more widespread and that, for every blatant case, there are scores of children who are malnourished.

Concerning kwashiorkor, Brock and Autret[43] found that an apathetic and peevish mentality was characteristic of this disease; and Clarke[59] was able to go much further when he wrote: "The mental changes found in kwashiorkor are the most consistent and probably some of the most important of all changes found in the disease. They are I think far more characteristic, constant and important than the skin changes about which so much has been written. A child with kwashiorkor is dull, apathetic and miserable. It rarely cries or screams, a low miserable whimper is the only vocal sign of its wretchedness ... Children with kwashiorkor are so dull and apathetic that if put to sit in one place will remain sitting there till lifted up again. They never, as do so many other children, go wandering off down the ward to investigate matters for themselves." Trowell[247] has emphasised the significance of this inertia at this crucial stage; and Davies[78] said: "A state of peevish apathy dominates the lives of many African children up to the age of five years—a period in which more favoured children are actively learning about the world around them, accommodating themselves to it, expanding and adjusting their personalities, and making their first social contacts. During this period, the African child is too often a whining, apathetic individual, and this must be a great handicap to his development."

Collis,[63] speaking of Nigerian children at the Pan-African Psychiatric Conference of 1961, said: "The mental symptoms associated with ... kwashiorkor tend to appear gradually. First, the child stops smiling, then he begins to cry more easily, he becomes unsocial, seems to lose all interest in everything; this is succeeded by apathy and active depression. Finally the child appears to reject life and will, if not treated vigorously, die quickly."

Stoch and Smythe's[240] valuable study of under-nourished Cape-Coloured children has already been discussed in regard to head circumference. In regard to intelligence it was found by tests that at all ages the mean of the under-nourished group was well below the control group and that the difference between the means remained relatively constant. At the final testing the mean I.Q. of the under-nourished group differed from that of the control group by 22·62 points, this being statistically significant ($t = 7·6$, $p <$ 0·01).

These writers measured the head circumferences and intelligence quotients of most of the parents and found no significant differences in the means of these for both groups, and concluded that "although these findings do not provide proof they are certainly suggestive that severe and prolonged under-nutrition during infancy can permanently retard brain growth and intellectual development".

What of the effects of malnutrition in adults? Keys and his confederates,[145] in their experiments at Minnesota, showed that prolonged semi-starvation of normal adults produced certain psychological effects. This experimental malnutrition was not fully comparable to malnutrition in Africa, since the former was essentially concerned with calorie lack, whereas the latter is mainly one of protein malnutrition. However, since calories are obtained from proteins (when not supplied from other sources) and since calorie lack is also not uncommon in Africa, especially at certain seasons, the relevance of this experiment remains considerable. Keys observed no significant objective deterioration of memory or logic: visual acuity and colour discrimination were not impaired; and auditory acuity was slightly, though definitely, increased. There was some impairment of neuromotor functions (strength, speed, and sustained power), but this may have been related to general bodily weakness and conservation of energy. The mental symptoms observed were largely interdependent, but can be grouped as follows:

(*a*) lassitude, with apathy, unsociability, and often depression:

(*b*) lack of sustained interest, with lack of drive and concentration; restriction of interest to food, and short-term egotism;

(*c*) emotional lability, with irritability, and lack of self-control and social inhibitions.

The relevance of these observations of Keys to the African scene becomes apparent when one turns to a study made by Collis[63] in Nigeria. Collis investigated the nutritional status of 4 village communities in the Western Region. Both calorie and protein insufficiencies were present in all these villages for at least one season in each year. The calorie situation improved in all the villages after harvest but in the poorer villages it never reached requirement levels, while the protein intake remained insufficient in all the villages all the time, the entire population in all the villages being in some degree in a state of permanent protein imbalance. Collis found that the people of the village with the best diet were cheerful, laughing, co-operative, and appeared to be vigorous, the children running and playing, and the adults working well; but that, in a village of poorer diet, the people showed a general lassitude and lack of sustained interest; and, in the village (Oke Ila) which had the poorest diet of all, the people were unsociable, suspicious, depressed, and apathetic.

Collis finally said:

"Keys, *et al.*, have noticed emotional lability, irritability, lack of self-control, and social inhibitions in the Minnesota observations of communities suffering from semi-starvation. We can confirm this in our Oke Ila village, though we would not care to be too dogmatic, being general physicians rather than psychiatrists. However, we are in no doubt that protein malnutrition, with or without calorie deficiency, produces a definite mental picture, characterised in its acute form by the acute mental depression seen in kwashiorkor, and the vaguer, yet quite demonstrable signs of apathy and unsociability in the pre-kwashiorkor state of protein imbalance. We submit then that these findings are of considerable importance in the assessing of the mental state of the people in the villages of the Western Region. Indeed, we would go so far as to suggest that unless one knows the nutritional state of any community, it may be misleading to attempt to assess their mental reactions."

This then was the picture observed by Collis, and his final remarks provide a perfect commentary on a situation which is undoubtedly a common one throughout the continent.

Psychology in relation to culture

(a) *The infant*

As far as the early months of life are concerned, the African infants' experience appears to be ideal. If later mental health depends on the infant experiencing "a warm, intimate and continuous relationship with his mother (or permanent mother substitute) in which both find satisfaction and enjoyment", as held by Bowlby,[41] this is just what the infant does experience. Moreover, since the mothers themselves were never likely to have suffered emotional deprivation, their ability to play their role in this relationship is likely to be unimpaired. Anything savouring of maternal rejection, overt or covert, must be rare and, in so far as it is possible to prolong the symbiosis of gestation into post-natal life, this is done.

If all later love and social feeling derive from one basic urge, a reciprocated attachment to the mother, as Suttie[242] believed, then these are likely to develop normally. The tensions observed by Ribble[218] in infants separated from their mothers, and the anxieties described by Sullivan[241] in infants whose mothers lack confidence and are anxious in their handling are not likely to arise. Ribble[218] has also shown that much of the cohesiveness of a child's personality depends on an emotional attachment to the mother which is built on tactile, kinaesthetic, and auditory experiences (by being fondled, rocked, carried, and talked to), and these are exactly what the African infant receives in full measure.

Therefore, in view of this general tolerance, and of the timing of maternal responses and teaching to the developing needs and abilities of the particular child, rather than to arbitrary times and ages, a situation is produced which appears to be ideally suited to infantile needs.

It has to be said, however, that this period of total indulgence may well be excessively prolonged. Thus for a long time the child hardly meets frustrations and has no opportunity to learn that "good things come to him who waits" at a time of life (the second year) when it may be important for him to do so. For, it is quite possible, as Ritchie[220] has postulated, that foresight and a sense of time in later life depend on learning of this sort at about this time of life.

In fact conscious memories commonly persist into adult African life of a period coloured by an illusion of omnipotence, and even sometimes of a period prior to the time when the distinction of the self from the environment develops. Kidd[146] gave a good example of the latter when he wrote:

> "One of the most intelligent Kaffirs I know told me that he could quite well remember his first headache during childhood. He said he was conscious that something was wrong somewhere, but did not dream that the pain was within his head. The pain might just as well have been in the roof of his hut as in the roof of his head; and it was only when his mother told him that his head was aching that this fact dawned upon him."

In regard to the persistence of the illusion of omnipotence, Prince[207] has much of interest to say. Writing of the Yoruba of Nigeria he says:

"An attempt has been made to show that in the evolution of thought, the ancestor of the word was the sign and the hallucination and that to the child the word and the sign and the hallucination are in a very concrete sense the same as the objects they represent. In the Western adult this stage of lack of distinction between inner fantasy and outer reality remains as a dimly remembered echo, whereas in the Yoruba it remains vividly conscious. It will be recalled that in the rituals of curse and invocation great emphasis is laid upon the mouth and its movements ... One might speculate that these activities are an attempt on the part of the Yoruba to recapture that Utopian era when the individual could master his universe through the movements of his own mouth.

"We might ask ourselves why the recollection of this oral omnipotence remains so strong in the Yoruba. There are perhaps a number of factors that might be suggested here. Perhaps the most important factor is that of prolonged breast feeding during childhood—the average Yoruba is breast fed until at least the age of two years, often until three or four. Many Yoruba can recall taking their mother's breast."

It is thus clear that this early blissful period is often so prolonged that it becomes ingrained in conscious memory and that this, among other implications, is likely to govern an attitude, often prominent in Africans, to the effect that the old times were the only good times. "Self demands and cultural demands must somehow be brought into mutual accordance" (Gesell and Ilg[114]); but whereas in Europe the cultural demands often impinge too early and too rigidly, in Africa they may be too delayed.

Weaning, as was shown before, is psychologically abrupt for the child, for he has had no previous experience of a type of frustration which many European infants experience several times a day almost from birth. Moreover, he commonly loses contact with his mother, both physically and emotionally, at this time. Faladé,[91] in her psychomotor study in Senegal, showed not only that weaning was traumatically abrupt there, but that it was followed by apathy in the child and a sudden arrest of his development which lasted for six to twelve months. It is possible, however, that malnutrition played some part in this.

Ritchie,[220] made the point that whereas previously infantile omnipotence was complete, the child is now thrust into a sense of total impotence and has no opportunity to reconcile these attitudes, so that henceforward the world for him is either wholly good and loving or wholly bad and hateful. Ritchie saw this as governing all later mental development in Africans and wrote: "As the world of reality denies his omnipotence, he is thrown back on the opposite conviction and remains helpless and psychically dependent on parents and parent surrogates all his days. His own individual personality, with all its latent powers, is never liberated and brought under conscious rational control, and self-realization is thus unknown to him."

Not all observers have agreed with Ritchie. Albino and Thompson,[4] for instance, in their study of the development of Zulu children, found that not only may abrupt weaning after long breast feeding be a disorganizing experience, but it may also serve as a powerful stimulus to ego development, at least if it occurs at the age of 18 months or later. Moreover, as Mead[177] has emphasized, since the maternal substitutes in traditional cultures are sure to carry much the same cultural assumptions as the child's mother, the break is likely to be much less dramatic than it seems.

In general Ritchie's approach seems to the present writer to be a valuable one. Later African development may well be partly explained on the lines of his argument. It is certainly common to meet Africans in the transitional working world who show only too clearly, and irritatingly, the tendency to oscillate between arrogance and humility that was described by Williams.[264] But Ritchie has probably attributed too much to infantile experience alone; the effects of this experience are probably not so irreversible as he envisaged.

(b) The child

To recapitulate; the father's relations with his child are remote at first though he is often important as an ideal, and punishment by him is used as a threat for misbehaviour. Punishment itself varies very much from tribe to tribe but it is likely that the threat of love-withdrawal as punishment by parents or parent substitutes is not used. Much learning is by unconscious assimilation of the behaviour patterns of the group one age-step ahead but, in so far as teaching is explicit, it is performed by a variety of persons —parents, older children, and other relations. Thus parental influence is much less exclusive than it commonly is in Europe, but education is given by a variety of persons, including the parents, whose influence is similar since they themselves were all products of the same process.

In Bateson's[15] words:

"For the establishment of an organized and more or less personified superego, such as we are familiar with in Western cultures: (a) the inculcation of cultural norms must be predominantly reinforced by punishment (including threats of withheld affection under this term); (b) the punishing role must be played by some individual adult (a parent or parent substitute); and (c) the behaviour of this punishing parent must be such that some species of close affective tie is established between the child and the parent."

Clearly Bateson's three conditions, and particularly the last, are seldom met in Africa. Wintrob and Wittkower[265] say that the superego is not structured as rapidly and severely as in the occident. One might go even further and say that it is hardly internalized in indigenous African life, its place being taken by the abiding authority of the group.

The whole Oedipal situation indeed probably follows different lines from those in Western societies, as emphasized in several psycho-analytic studies. Collomb[67] has maintained this, and also said that as the father is of such high status—representing the ancestors, law and social order—it is considered impossible to compete with him. Parin *et al.*[196] from their psycho-analytic study of Dogon men in Mali, believe that, due to the traumatic weaning experience, the fear of castration by the father is replaced by a fear of loss of the mother which is in later life transformed into a fear of being abandoned by the wife; and that the child identifies after weaning with various of his brothers, peers, relations, parents, and ancestors, thus developing an ego and a superego which are "of the group". The Ortigues,[192] in a psychoanalytic study of Africans of Senegal, also found in regard to the Oedipus complex that rivalry of the son with the father seemed to be systematically displaced on to members of the peer group, who became the target for aggressive drives.

Education of the child is particularly directed towards inculcating codes of manners, deportment, and behaviour in regard to the child's relations to a far remove. He has to learn many names and degrees of relationship, since his behaviour must be adjusted to each social context. Indeed his teaching in general is concerned with meticulous rules of behaviour in a host of concrete situations.

This sort of teaching is easy for children, with their good

imitative powers and good rote memories, to assimilate. Thus, as the child progresses in life he knows just how to behave in all the social contexts he is likely to meet, and so acquires early a social self-confidence and maturity of manner which would be enviable in European children, who often have to work things out for themselves, on the basis of a few general rules, in much more varied social contexts. However, since so much emphasis is placed upon good manners and on avoiding the giving of offence, the highest truth is often the version that is deemed most likely to be acceptable to the hearer. And since ethical behaviour is firmly rooted in the family and clan, it has no application to complete outsiders. Thus, ethical ideals such as diligence, courage, and hospitality, are not lacking, but their fields of application are limited.

The following record of a Court case at which the present writer attended is inserted here, partly for light-relief, partly to illustrate several points that have been mentioned.

A little African girl aged about 9 years was giving evidence in a case in which her brother had been killed. The judge began by asking her a number of questions to satisfy himself that she had sufficient capacity to be affirmed.

Q. "Have you any religion?"
A. "No."
Q. "Have you ever been to school?"
A. "No."
Q. "Has anyone ever taught you anything and if so what?"
A. "My mother teaches me how people should grow up and to be polite and to obey."
Q. "Do you know the difference between right and wrong?"
A. "No."
Q. "Do you know the difference between truth and falsehood?"
A. "Yes, if you tell lies people will say you told lies and if you tell the truth people will say you have told the truth."

The judge then decided she had sufficient capacity to be affirmed, and she proceeded to give very damning evidence against the accused. Finally, in answer to questions, she said:

"Yes, my mother was very angry because my brother was killed and she wants the accused to be killed." "Yes, I her daughter also want the accused to be killed." Judge: "So you have come here to give as strong evidence against him as you can?" The girl, "Yes."

Games are not organized by adults, and there are virtually no toys. Toy building blocks, jig-saw puzzles, and the host of mechanical toys and objects (keys, switches, taps, handles, etc.) that form the normal environment of children in the urban West are lacking.

The child is thus never encouraged to manipulate those elements of the spatio-temporal world on which are later based the concepts of mechanical causation which form the constant background of life and thought in western Europe. Stephen and Robertson,[238] writing of European children, say:

"As the child grows older, the awareness of perceptual constancies develops. Size, distance, etc., can be judged, culminating in the ability to deal with spatial relationships. Detailed information about the development of these skills is scanty, but we do have information about the cues ultimately used in making judgements. The use of these cues must develop through long periods of trial and error, of having one's expectancies more and more frequently confirmed."

It is most likely that the lack of this type of experience in early childhood can hardly be redressed by later learning; also this plays a part at least in the manifest difficulty experienced by many African adults, who are bright in other ways, to envisage solid objects 3-dimensionally and manipulate them effectively.

There is a high level of knowledge of the objective world in several fields; in agriculture, animal husbandry, and hut-building for instance; and much of this knowledge is imparted to the child in a logical way. But causation, where this is unknown, is explained on magical and animistic lines which tend to become fixed and ritualized and unamenable to criticism. As compared with the West there is little specialization, so that the older child is liable to find himself substantially in command of the objective knowledge of his group. In the absence of recorded history, tribal history tends quickly to become mythical.

Piaget's studies[203] of European children are highly relevant to the problem of the mental development of the child in Africa; a fact which was recognized by Dougall[84] in a very illuminating article 40 years ago. Piaget found that about the age of 7 or 8 years children moved from a stage in which thinking was essentially egocentric to one of an increasing objectivity. In the earlier stage childish explanations are marked by a high degree of subjectivity; events occur to help or to defeat oneself, they occur by reason of motives like one's own; and causal connection is implied, not only by contiguity in space or time, but by obvious similarities without such contiguity. In general, such thinking is "magical" and later "animistic"; general principles are not considered, anything is possible, and the world is governed both in material and social matters by "personal wills". In the later stage there is a conscious recognition of the need to ask the question "How?" In the conception of causality, the need is seen for continuity and contact, for things to derive from other things, for the birth of new events by reassortment of parts or qualities and, at last, for explanation by spatial and temporal relations and for logical deduction. It is during this period that generality of principle first appears and necessity becomes not only moral but physically deterministic.

It has to be noted that the elements of the first stage, which gradually disappear from the thinking of the European child after the age of 7 or 8 years, remain prominent in the thinking of adults in rural Africa.

It has, however, also to be noted that, whether or not the African child is *capable* of leaving the earlier stage behind (a matter which is not under discussion at this point), he is given no opportunity to do so by the nature of the culture in which he grows up. For, inasmuch as explanations are forthcoming, they are commonly given on mythical, magical, and animistic lines which, though well suited to the needs of little children everywhere, are both too facile and too final, and stifle curiosity in children who might otherwise view the unknown as a challenge.

The mechanical toys, devices, and the machines which surround the European child familiarize him from an early age with the facts of mechanical causation. He soon comes to know that pressing a button rings, through a wire, the distant bell, that toy motor cars must be wound and that events in general are explicable on mechanical lines. In these achievements he is not discouraged by his seniors and, throughout his schooling, they form much of the basis of his formal education. He is encouraged to integrate his knowledge and to depend on the appropriate application of general principles and, in face of the diversity of modern knowledge, needs no reminding of his ignorance, or of the fact that he has far to go.

For the rural African child, however, the world remains a place where events are governed by mysterious and wayward "wills". He soon also comes to know that it is little less mysterious for his seniors than it is for him, that he stands at much the same point as these—face to face with the unknowable—and that, although he feels some awe in regard to this, it is a feeling that is shared by all his group.

In view of this; in view of his general social training as described before, and in contrast to his sense of personal impotence in regard to the world at large, the child thus acquires a social confidence and competence which, from a European point of view, is far beyond his years.

There is, of course, no reading or writing. Teaching is by the spoken word and this, as the present writer has contended elsewhere,[54] is of its nature more dynamic, emotional, and personal than is the written word. It was thus not until the word, with writing, moved into the more static, objective and impersonal visual world that it became possible for man to see that words were symbols only, that verbal thought was separable from action, and not until this point was reached that "omnipotence of thought" received its death blow. Without this development, verbal thought on unique personal lines remains a fearful thing, a thing to be eschewed. But this theme, as it seems to the present writer, is of such importance for African psychology at all ages that it will be discussed at greater length at the end of this chapter.

(c) The adolescent

Blanchard,[34] writing of adolescent experience in general, says: "From whatever viewpoint adolescence is regarded, it seems to be agreed, with but few exceptions, that the changes in the physiological organism that take place at puberty result in reinforcement of heterosexual drives and of strivings for independence and personal responsibility."

Warren[258] says:

"Briefly, puberty leads to a recrudescence and heightening of the
sexual drive, genitality now coming to the fore. . . . Besides sexuality, the adolescent's intellectual life now becomes enriched by an
influx of new interests and then attitudes, often highly emotionally
toned. They may be of short duration but meanwhile, perhaps
running contrary to the parents' viewpoint, give rise to disapproval
and so to clashes between them. . . . Growth of independence is
important, as successful emancipation from the family is necessary
to achieve maturity. Adolescents strive towards this, although at the
same time there may well be a harking back to the security of
childhood. . . . Most adolescents gain security from associating with
their peers."

As far as African life is concerned, the need for sex outlets are
well recognized from an early age and these are permitted within
well-defined limits for each period of life. At puberty, if not
before, sex instruction is explicit, and the manifold embarrass-
ments, conflicts and anxieties that may derive from lack of this in
the West are uncommon in Africa.

Over large areas initiatory rituals and ceremonies mark the
advancement of the adolescent into responsible membership of
the tribe, with the increase of rights and duties that this entails.

The strivings for independence, mentioned by both the above
authorities, are probably felt in some degree by adolescents
everywhere. In Herskovitz's words;[125] "This tugging of the
young at the reins by which the old try to hold them on the
cultural roadway they themselves have travelled, is a constant in
human social life." It is therefore of interest to note that where
initiatory rituals are severe, as is the case in many parts of Africa,
they seem to have as one aim (as Raum[217] has suggested in regard
to the Chaga) to suppress any independence of spirit the young
folk may still possess, and to act as a final firm reminder that they
are still subordinate to their elders. The effects of this are,
however, mitigated and the aim itself disguised by the considerable increase of heterosexual activity which is encouraged at this
time.

(d)   The adult

Although the adult still has things to learn, particularly about
the religious and ritualistic aspects of his culture (and about his
craft if he is to be a craftsman), he is by now well versed in all its

more practical aspects and has acquired a vested interest in the maintenance of his culture. Adult prestige in Africa is precariously based and must be jealously guarded by a firm adherence to the rules; by a conformity which has, among other things, become a duty to oneself.

Anxieties are never far from the surface. They are partly "natural". Disease and death, droughts, the death of stock, the failure of crops are familiar experiences which impinge very directly upon the people. The world in general is an inimical one; there are dangerous beasts and insects, poisonous plants and fish, alien and inevitably hostile tribes, and persons of ill-will, real or imagined, within one's own tribe. All these are seen as possessed of "powers", mainly malevolent, which can only be combated by the "power" within oneself or by other powers that might be tapped through, say, the witchdoctor.

Apart from these natural fears, however, are super-added others which form the subject of this paragraph. All activities have to be considered by the subject from the point of view of the rights of some third party and, if things go wrong, this is seen as probably due to one's having offended one of these. Conformity in these matters is enforced by public opinion, by the will of the elders and above all, by the "will" of the deceased ancestors who are seen as having the greatest power of all, the more so for acting mysteriously and invisibly. Thus, when misfortune comes, the fear of having transgressed a rule and given offence is added to any real dangers that may exist. Fear of bewitchment is hardly separable from this; it lurks continually in the background and when it comes to the surface is often based, not so much on evidence of witchcraft, as on a half-conscious recognition of some antisocial act committed by oneself. Even outstanding success gives rise to this fear.

Various cultural mechanisms—ritual outlets, dances, preparation for various stages of life, specifies against particular dangers—ease the burden of this anxiety and function as safety valves, as Biesheuvel[24] has emphasized. Bereavement also is not borne in isolation and sorrows in general are shared. Frequent resort is also made to the witch-doctor, not only for protection but to achieve one's positive aims.

Thus Lambo[152] found among 1,300 Nigerian schoolchildren that 1,105 (85 per cent) "used some kind of native medicine to help them pass examinations, to be liked by the teachers and to ward off the evil effects of other students' 'medicines' which were intended to retard their progress", and he goes on to say that an "almost fanatical faith in the magic of certain symbols to produce desired results is not confined to the preliterate Nigerian or to the young schoolchildren but it permeates the entire society".

Westermann[259] wrote: "The world of the primitive African is characterized by its unity and coherence. No sharply defined aspect exists by itself; wish and reality, the possible and the impossible, knowledge and belief, thought and imagination, the realms of secular and religious life are interwoven and fundamentally one." Thoughts and dreams could well have been included, and the lack of distinction between body and mind is commonly seen in psychiatric practice, as will be shown.

Viewing these matters broadly it can be seen that a man's stability is highly dependent on the continuing support afforded by his culture and has but little independent existence in himself. Rapaport,[216] referring to the development of consciousness in general, says: "the gradual development to thought as 'experimental action' from thought as 'hallucinatory gratification' reflects the gradual development from monoideic consciousness of drive gratification to polyideic consciousness of the relation of perceived external reality, internal need, and memories of past experiences." African adult psychology might thus be described as monoideic for, in dealing with any situation for which no pattern of behaviour is prescribed by local custom, such behaviour is apt to be impulsive and marked by concentration on immediately presenting aspects of that situation, without regard for the sum of stored experience or for its future implications. But it has to be noted that this only becomes apparent when a man steps forth from his traditional world.

*   *   *

The psychology of African peoples has been described in this section against the background of their culture, particularly in so far as the latter differs from that of western Europe. The psychology that results can on this basis be assessed in one of two ways. It can be assessed in its relationship to life in either the traditional way or the Western way. But the former would now seem to be a rather pointless pastime. Whether or not African peoples are going to go the Western way, or the Eastern way, or some other way of their own, it is most likely that animistic modes of thought, for instance, will decline and that literacy has come to stay. The African traditional way *might* be the best way of life for Africa if that continent were left in isolation, or if its people were content to be so left, but this is so far from being the case that the cultural modes described are already disintegrating. Moreover, in the present writer's view, the African and European cultural modes are not to be seen as parallel achievements, for the former can in many of its features best be seen as a stage of cultural development which European peoples followed in the past, but passed beyond. It is therefore legitimate to view the problem in relation to a man's adaptability for a world of accelerating change.

The cultural background described above, and the psychology that develops on that basis, results in a man being integrated very completely into his society. So that, within his society he is seldom at a loss and is courageous, loyal, stoical, socially self-confident and eloquent, courteous, and very sensitive to the feelings of others. All this is clearly admirable, but it is achieved at the expense of integration at the personal intellectual level. A man is not expected to think for himself except in regard to the practical details of living and lacks principles of general application on which such integration could occur. He thus becomes intellectually conventional and does not see himself as a self-reliant unit with sustained responsibility for all his deeds, past, present, and future, but rather as a puppet pulled by interpersonal strings. In the new environment, as the present writer[51] has shown, routine procedures are followed blindly, little attempt is made to see events as elements in a meaningful total situation, and an attitude of over-confidence tends to alternate with one of impotence. Whether or not intellectual curiosity, independence of thought, initiative, and personal responsibility for one's acts are to be regarded as virtues, they are certainly required for successful living in the Western way and, as such, must be acquired by people who aim to go that way.

Now although cultures act as wholes, and although all the cultural features described interact to produce the psychology of African peoples, it is the present writer's view that it is the lack of the written word that is the factor of transcendent cultural importance for mental development that distinguishes the

African from the European mode. It may even govern cerebral
development. It would after all be rather surprising if the acquisition of the written word by man played a part that was other than
cardinal for his development. Few people would deny that the
supremacy of man as a species was the outcome of his development of verbal thought, for it was surely his ability to abstract
from his experience, to store his abstractions economically, and to
communicate them—abilities dependent upon words—that raised
him to the new biological plane. The development of writing
could be seen as a step of rather comparable import for, not only
does this step entail the great enhancement of all those elements
that make words valuable (abstraction, storage, communication)—
a quantitative advance; but, as is indicated below, it alters the
quality of thought itself.

The argument, which was fully developed in an earlier article,[54]
takes the following course. The word and verbal thought in
general are conceived in non-literate African societies as having
existence in their own right, with powers and vulnerabilities of the
same order as the events or acts for which they stand. They are
seen, in other words, as being "behavioural" in the same sense as
any other form of action. Much magic incorporates this principle
and "evil-willing", for instance, is, after all, the most fearful type
of "behaviour" known in Africa. In Prince's[207] words: "Thought
without word has no potency. This is made clear by discussion
with contemporary Yoruba and is confirmed by the practice in
former times of gagging the victims to be used for human sacrifice
so that they cannot utter imprecations upon their captors", and the
present writer[53], has described how the strength of the Mau Mau
oaths in Kenya depended largely on the belief that recantation
would result in instant death from the "power" of the oaths alone.

Non-literate societies live largely in a world of sound in contrast
to literate societies who live largely in a world of vision. Sounds
are of their nature dynamic things or indicators of dynamic
things—of movements, events, activities for which man, when
largely unprotected from the hazards of life in the bush must be
ever on the alert. Whereas in the urban West people develop and
must develop an ability for ignoring sounds, in this rural setting
they are not to be ignored for they are usually of direct significance for the hearer. Particularly is this true of the human voice,
for the spoken word when heard is usually directed to the hearer,
and contains personal and emotional elements which are always

recognizable. The world of sound in other words, is a relatively subjective, personal, and emotional world.

When words are written they move, of course, into the visual world. Like most of the latter's elements they then become static things and lose, as such, much of the dynamism which is so characteristic of the auditory world in general and of the spoken word in particular; and they lose much of the personal element in that they are now seldom directed at oneself. They lose the emotional overtones and emphases which are such an integral part of vocal speech and can much more easily be misinterpreted according to the reader's understanding or his prejudice. They thus, in general, join a world of relative indifference to the viewer—a world wherein they can be seen so much more easily for what they are—symbols, without existence in their own right. Thus, it was only at this point that it became easy for man to see that verbal thought is not of its nature behavioural, but is separable from action.

Although at first sight it might not seem important whether mankind was introduced more insistently to the world of sight or the world of sound, it is in fact of fundamental importance. For living effectively in the modern Western world, a well-developed sense of spatio-temporal relations and of causal relationship on mechanistic lines is required, and this is highly dependent on a habit of visual, as opposed to auditory, synthesis. The world of magic, governed by animistic "powers" could, it is believed, pass away only when man's attention became focused more emphatically on the relatively objective, continuous, and irrelevant visual world. Admittedly social literacy is seldom an all-or-none phenomenon. But there does seem to come a point in the literate development of societies where the society as a whole takes its climate of thought from its literate members, and the magical ideology decays, as happened for instance with the ancient Greeks, and, much later, in Renaissance Europe.

A development such as this has important implications for socio-cultural development. All societies must achieve some measure of behavioural conformity in their members but their manner of achieving this will vary and will depend in the first instance on the attitude in each society in regard to the relation of thought and deed. For in those societies where *no* sharp distinction has been made between verbal thought and action, "behavioural" constraints *must* include constraint of thought; whereas those societies which recognize that thought is separable from action *need not* attempt to constrain their members at the level of their thinking. The constraint of thought in the former case is achieved automatically in the several ways described earlier, and especially by the finality of magical and animistic explanations, by the need to be governed by the "will" of others, and by fears of bewitchment. It is done without sophisticated appreciation of the effects of the achievement, but all the more effectively for that. Its effects, however, are such that a man becomes afraid to speculate on unique personal lines, becomes highly extrovert, and tends to see such unorthodox thoughts as do occur to him as deriving from alien or even evil sources. Whereas in societies where this constraint is not a dominant one, the individual comes to see himself as entitled to think for himself and as responsible for his own thoughts and deeds.

That man in western Europe has indeed moved psychologically from an earlier (pre-Renaissance) "ear culture" to a later "eye culture" and that this movement was related, first, to the invention of a phonetic alphabet and, secondly, to the invention of printing, has been made abundantly clear in the immensely thought-provoking writings of McLuhan.[176] Parts of the argument developed above are therefore strongly supported by one who writes from the very different viewpoint of a professor of English literature and whose data, accordingly, are largely literary and historical.

African mental development is, in the present writer's view, largely to be explained on these grounds. Man in Africa is, by the nature of his cultural experience, fitted marvellously well into his society from an early age, but this is done at the expense of his adaptability in later life for other cultural modes.

It is even possible that this cultural experience might of itself truncate cerebral development concurrently with mental. Whether or not Vint's [253, 254] findings were the result of genetic, nutritional and/or environmental factors his studies of African brains led him to conclude that the stage of cerebral development reached by the average African was that of the average European boy of between 7 and 8 years of age. Vint's subjects were mainly, if not entirely, without formal education of European type and he emphasized that the differences he observed were due, not to a lack of cerebral cells, but to their immaturity, and that it was "impossible to say how many would mature under conditions of life and education different to those which normally obtain today". Piaget's work is also relevant to this issue for he[203] observed that European children, at about the age of 7 or 8 years, move from a stage where thought is magical and animistic to a stage where it is based on spatio-temporal relations and physical determinism. Observations such as these impel the question as to whether it is mere coincidence that at about the age of 7 or 8 European children have fully acquired the art of reading; and whether it is not possible that the maturation of those cortical cells in Europeans is dependent on the acquisition of this art, and of the release of thought which seems to stem from the recognition of its impotence.

Psychology of the American Negro

Any attempt to elucidate the nature-nurture issue in regard to African psychology must lead to an enquiry into the psychology of the Negro in America. For, in theory at least, knowledge of how the Negro shapes in other lands might throw light on how far peculiarities observed in Africa are innate. In the United States, for instance, the Negro now shares with the Whites a common language and a common way of life; a state of affairs which only applies to selected groups in Africa. Moreover, much thought has been given to this question in the States where, as is well known, the problem has important practical implications and where, accordingly, an extensive relevant literature has appeared in recent years.

Here also, however, the problem is not simple, and this for two major reasons. First, largely for the historical reasons cited earlier, the Negro in the States lives on the whole, and compared with the Whites, at a lower socio-economic level; his educational opportunities in the past were inferior, and his occupational opportunities have been fewer, and the latter in its turn has limited his educational incentives. Secondly, few American Negroes today are of pure Negro ancestry; perhaps about 22 per cent according to an estimate quoted earlier; but it is probably correct to assume that if differences that might be racial do emerge, they are merely diminished by this fact.

It can be said at once that, in terms of school achievement, American Negroes do not on average rise to the standard of American Whites. Thus Osborne[193] records:

"On group achievement tests designed to evaluate the degree of success in learning the basic subjects taught in public schools, the American Negro with rare exception is unable to keep pace with established grade norms. In most subjects the average Negro child falls behind the norm group at the rate of almost one-third of a grade per year, until by the time he graduates from high school he is in some areas four full years below the twelfth grade standard."

One has to ask whether this is due to a lack of general intelligence in American Negroes as compared with American Whites; a question which leads to a consideration of the intelligence testing of these groups in America.

As to whether intelligence tests can ever really throw light on innate (as well as measuring acquired) abilities—a matter which is still sometimes disputed—Eysenck[89] is well worth quoting. He wrote:

> "Do tests of mental ability in fact tap innate factors? The evidence is by now quite conclusive that they are surprisingly successful in doing so. Consider a recent study by James Shields, in which he administered two intelligence tests to groups of fraternal twins brought up together, and to identical twins some of whom had been brought up separately. Identical twins share completely a common heredity, while fraternal twins are only 50 per cent alike with respect to heredity; on the tests the identical twins were found to be more than twice as similar to each other, whether brought up together or separate, then were the fraternal twins."

Of course, much depends on what is implied by separation; on the degree of difference in experience entailed. The present writer has not read Shields' article, but it is fairly safe to assume that his identical twins brought up separately were nevertheless brought up within roughly similar cultural environments. The relatively high degree of similarity he found in these twins would surely not be found where one was reared among, say, rural Africans in Africa and the other among urban Europeans. Innate factors, in other words, would be very difficult to tap by tests of Negroes and Whites in the African setting. On the other hand there would seem to be no reason why they could not be tapped in the Negro-White setting of the States.

Intelligence testing has been vigorously practised in the United States during the last six decades and, as far as this was concerned with the testing of Negroes—a matter involving hundreds of thousands of children and adults—it has been very fully and meticulously summarized by Shuey.[227] In assessing the results among children and students, she found that the mean I.Q. of the Negroes was consistently less than that of the Whites, to the extent of about 12 points in the pre-school children, of about $14\frac{1}{2}$ points in the schoolchildren, and of about 15 points in the High School students; and that Negro College students achieved average scores which placed them from about the 6th to the 13th percentile rank (according to the various tests used) of the White norms. In regard to those studies in which the amount of overlapping was reported or could be determined, the degree of this overlap (on the percentage of Negroes who achieved scores higher than the White average) was 12 per cent in school-children, 10 per cent in High school students, and 7 per cent in College students. An overall assessment of the great number of studies that have been made on Negro children and adults showed results which were remarkably consistent with each other and which, in terms of mean I.Q., could be expressed as approximating to 85; a figure which is to be compared with a mean for Whites of 100. Shuey concluded by marshalling all the arguments raised in her monumental work and, in what must be one of the longest sentences ever penned in the English language (and which cannot therefore be fully recorded here), wrote: "The remarkable consistency in test results" taken together with all these arguments "inevitably point to the presence of native differences between Negroes and Whites as determined by intelligence tests".

Professor Corrado Gini[116], reviewing the first edition of this book, said:

> "Does Professor Shuey's volume furnish the basis, until now lacking, to establish the existence of innate racial differences even in the sphere of mental abilities? ... it is possible to say that, because of the abundance of the material collected and objectively reported, the volume constitutes a milestone in this area. After its publication the burden of proof rests upon those who maintain the non-existence of the stated differences."

Perhaps the strongest argument in support of a purely cultural explanation of the observed differences in intelligence by tests would be the demonstration of a clear tendency for these differences to diminish in step with a diminution of the cultural differences. Klineberg has been one of the chief exponents of the cultural explanation. He wrote:[147]

> "The net result of all the research that has been conducted in this field is that there is no scientific proof of innate racial differences in intelligence; that the obtained differences in test results are best explained in terms of factors in the social and educational environment; that as the environmental opportunities of different racial or ethnic groups become more similar, the observed differences in test results also tend to disappear."

But does this statement now accord with the facts? McGurk[175] has compared the test status of Negroes tested in World War I with that of Negroes tested in the six studies made between 1935 and 1951 which could be compared with the earlier study. It had been found in the World War I tests that only about 27 per cent of the Negro recruits obtained scores that equalled or exceeded the mean score of the White recruits. The comparable figures in the 6 subsequent studies varied from about 17 per cent to 31 per cent. The last of these studies was one of his own in which the figure came to 28 per cent. He writes:[175]

> "The cultural position of the Negro has certainly improved since 1918. This improvement has not been sudden, but has been in progress for at least two generations. The Negro has achieved more and more of the social and economic opportunities that were once reserved for the White man, and to say that the cultural status of the Negro has not improved markedly is to deny objective evidence .... In spite of the socio-economic equivalence, Negro overlapping for total score was only 28 per cent—a figure almost identical with that reported for the World War I data. There is no question about the cultural superiority of the Negroes in 1951 over the Negroes in 1918. Yet this did not improve the Negro's test performance at all. Thus, in the 16 years between 1935 and 1950, a period of unquestioned cultural advancement for the Negro (compared with World War I period), there can be found no factual evidence to support the claim that equalizing the cultural opportunities of the two races results in equalizing their psychological test scores, or even reducing the racial test score difference. On the basis of the only studies available for this comparison, it must be concluded that the culture hypothesis must be rejected."

McGurk emphasizes finally that it is not his contention that the culture hypothesis is incorrect, but that it possesses no factual validity and is contradicted by the available evidence.

It should be made clear at this point that, although few if any students of this problem would claim that observed racial differences in intelligence were *exclusively* genetic, many have claimed that they were exclusively environmental (or socio-cultural in the American setting). Thus, when McGurk refers to the "culture hypothesis", he is referring to a hypothesis that carries this exclusive connotation, as is clear from the definition he gives elsewhere in his article. His references to that hypothesis must therefore be read in that sense.

There remains an aspect of intelligence testing which is very pertinent to this study—the problem of culture-free tests. As Eysenck[90] has pointed out, although there are at present no culture-free tests, the tests we do have can be graded on a continuum, with those that are relatively culture free (particularly non-verbal tests dependent on the eduction of relations) at one end and those that are highly culture bound (particularly verbal tests dependent on school learning) at the other. On the theory that intelligence is mainly environmentally determined, one would expect a group which is at an environmental disadvantage (poor home, education, etc.) to perform better on tests that are relatively culture free (or culture fair) than on tests that are not. This concept is an important one and its application to the problem of racial intelligence has produced some surprising results. Thus it has been shown in America that, although certain other racial groups (e.g. Mexican-Americans of very low socio-economic status) respond as expected by achieving higher scores on relatively culture-free tests than on culture bound ones, the reverse is true of American Negroes. This finding is, as Eysenck has remarked, difficult to account for in purely environmental terms.

In regard to particular tests, Shuey[227] found that "in general, Negroes have been reported as earning their best scores in tests identified as purposeful, practical, and concrete, and as achieving their lowest scores in tests that involve logical analysis, abstract reasoning, and certain perceptual-motor functions". It is particularly interesting to note that tests involving spatial understanding and manipulation, such as Koh's Block Design test, are found especially difficult, since this has also been observed in African Negroes.

For the assessment of faculties other than intellectual, the Rorschach test has been widely used in recent decades, though surprisingly seldom in comparative studies of Negroes and Whites in America. However, Hunter,[129] in a Rorschach study of 100 Whites and 100 Negroes in New York city, found that "the number of Negroes who are introversive was only 60 per cent of the number among the Whites who were introversive"; and Price[206] found in a study of 90 White and 90 Negro children in Florida a stronger trend towards introversion with increasing age in the White children, and concluded in general that "the younger children and Negroes seem to function in a somewhat less inhibited or controlled and less complex manner in the emotional sphere".

In sum, the American evidence goes to show that differences between Whites and Negroes exist, both in intellectual and temperamental faculties. It also shows that, in tests devised to assess the sort of abilities which are prized by all races in the Western world, the overall achievement of the average American Negro is less than that of the average American White. Finally, it is clearly becoming increasingly difficult to explain the latter wholly on environmental grounds. How far these findings are relevant to the Negro in Africa will be discussed in the final chapter.

Psychiatry

Aetiology

Causation in African psychiatry can be assumed to follow general principles which are the same as those elsewhere. It can be discussed therefore under the headings of hereditary and environmental factors but, since the former doubtless follow familiar patterns on the whole and since the latter have been surveyed in an earlier chapter, a few points only will be mentioned here.

Hereditary factors

African culture, with its insistence on conformity and its discouragement of curiosity and initiative, might enable many people, who would be regarded as defective in the urban societies of the West, to pass muster in the community. Gordon[118] postulated that these people multiplied excessively in indigenous life due to selective elimination of the more courageous and adventurous (in tribal warfare and in conflicts with animal predators) and had thus progressively lowered the mean of general intelligence.

On the other hand polygyny in Africa is related to paternal success. Thus, although in African life there is little scope for the expression of brilliance at other than practical levels, it is in general likely that material success and a disproportionately large number of offspring have accrued to the more intelligent fathers. This factor might therefore operate progressively to raise the mean of general intelligence.

Thus it is likely that cultural factors have played a part in influencing the mental heritage of Africans; but it is by no means clear what their final influence has been.

Environmental factors

The part played by infections is a large one, as was shown in Chapter 3. Whereas some of these, like trypanosomiasis, syphilis, and cerebral malaria, produce effects which are specific and determinable, others simply produce a background of ill health or anaemia which must predispose to mental disturbance or aggravate it later.

Malnutrition, apart from pellagra, probably also plays a part which is as important as it is often insidious. Malnutrition in pre-natal life and infancy may interfere with neurone development and, in early childhood, may incapacitate the children at the very time when they should be most adventurous and curious and, in either case, result in a backwardness which is partly irreversible. In later life a state of chronic undernutrition and anaemia may predispose to the development of neuroses and psychoses and must leave the subject with so little margin that a short period of famine will precipitate pellagra. Finally, any mental condition which results in deficient food intake (such as depression) or excessive energy output (such as mania) is also liable to result in frank pellagra.

Alcohol is mainly consumed in the forms of millet beer or palm wine. Spirits are little drunk except in townships. Although the beers and wines are of a low alcohol content, they are imbibed at social events in such amounts that intoxication is common, with results that are more often criminal than psychiatric.

Finally, cultural factors are of the greatest importance for psychiatry, but are more appropriately referred to under the headings of incidence or of the psychiatric categories described later in this chapter.

Epidemiology

Any attempt to write about the epidemiology of mental illness in Africa runs immediately into formidable difficulties. These difficulties are formidable enough even in such countries as England and Wales where, for instance, few of the markedly defective or seriously disturbed, fail to come to the notice of authority, and where people have come to know that mental disturbance is a form of illness amenable to medical help. But in Africa the problem is of another order. So much so, indeed, that one had best admit at the outset, that no studies of the statistics of mental illness in Africa can be made at present on lines that are at all strictly comparable with studies made in western Europe or America.

Yet, if one waits until the strict comparisons *can* be made, one will have waited till much of the value of the study has probably been lost. The attempt must therefore be made, as indeed it has been made before. First, however, it is essential to say something of the difficulties that beset psychiatric epidemiology in Africa.

An epidemiological study of the type dealt with in this chapter is concerned with figures recorded in reports and articles; figures which in this context refer to cases of mental illness (psychotic, neurotic, or psycho-somatic) or mental defect, seen in particular circumstances. Yet the circumstances in which the cases were seen were often not strictly comparable with the circumstances in other series of cases, and the cases themselves were often not categorized in comparable terms. Often, indeed, neither the circumstances nor the criteria of diagnosis were adequately described. This is generally true throughout the world to the degree that the W.H.O. Expert Committee on Mental Health in its Third Report[260] was able to write: "One of the difficulties which the Committee faces in making recommendations for the provision of psychiatric medical care is that there is little exact information on the extent of psychiatric morbidity. . . . This epidemiological approach to the problem of psychiatric disorders has hitherto been almost completely neglected." If this is true in general, it is still more true in Africa, and the problem there can best be discussed under two main headings: first, the circumstances; and secondly, the cases.

In regard to the circumstances, most figures in Africa refer to mental hospital in-patients, either as first admissions over a stated period, or as cases in hospital at a certain time. The resulting figures are of much interest, but, taken by themselves as measures of total incidence or prevalence, are valueless for purposes of comparison with figures of incidence or prevalence in Western countries. They are even valueless for purposes of comparison with total in-patient figures in these countries. Quite often the African mental hospital referred to is the only mental hospital of the country concerned. Thus the reader might be led to assume that all the cases requiring in-patient care from that country would come under scrutiny there. In practice, however, this is very far from being the case. Even in England, where institutional care for the mentally disturbed has been long established, it is not entirely true, but in the relatively undeveloped parts of the world referred to in this chapter it is almost entirely untrue, for accommodation lags far behind the need.

The circumstances that govern the admission of psychiatric cases in Africa are first, criminality; secondly, proximity to the mental hospital; thirdly, "Westernization" with recognition of the advantages of institutional care; and fourthly, difficulty in home care. And in regard to the last item, persons are more difficult to look after at home (or may even be homeless) if they work in townships, if they are alien immigrants, if they belong to the male sex, if they are adults of young or middle age, or if their mental disturbance takes a menacing or violent form.

South African figures are, on the face of it, likely to be the best for purposes of comparison since the organization of psychiatric care has developed for longer here than elsewhere south of the Sahara, and since large populations of Whites as well as Africans are being catered for. But here again there is a relative shortage of accommodation for Africans as shown by Lamont and Blignault for Weskoppies Hospital[154], and by the Annual Report of the South African Commissioner for Mental Hygiene[236] for the country in general.

A few studies have also been made of cases, particularly neuroses, seen at general or day hospitals, and of military personnel with particular reference to West Africa. These studies will be referred to again, but none of them lend themselves easily to use for epidemiological purposes.

Urgently required are studies in the field and, in fact, a small number of these have been made, the circumstances varying greatly in each study. Such studies bring one much nearer to the heart of the problem and, taken in conjunction with the hospital cases, could produce figures for fair comparison with European figures. These studies will therefore be described later at greater length but, to anticipate a little, it has to be said that even these do not, and cannot, fail to run into the sort of difficulties that are described under the second heading—the cases.

As regards the cases, difficulties arise at two main levels; the first being that what constitutes a case—a patient, a person needing psychiatric help—is something very different in Africa from what it is in Europe; while the second concerns the diagnosis when the case *is* seen.

In regard to the first problem, attendance at a mental hospital in the circumstances of life in Africa is governed not only by the social factors described earlier, but by the question of what is regarded as normal or abnormal behaviour in each society, and what degree of deviance from the orthodox standards is accepted by the society concerned. This problem has been discussed by several writers and the W.H.O. Expert Committee in its Eighth Report,[261] wrote that "there are considerable social and cultural differences in what is considered psychically abnormal in different surroundings, and in the way such abnormality is treated. This depends on the attitude of the community to unusual behaviour, its opinions about the value of psychiatric care, and the facilities for such care which are actually available." Thus, a person with a facility for dissociation, who in England would be regarded as "suffering" from an hysterical personality, would in Africa often be regarded with veneration and as qualified thereby to become a practitioner of medicine. Epilepsy, on the other hand, is viewed in many parts of Africa with such fear of its contagiousness that other patients in the same hospital are likely to leave rather than risk contamination.

In general, African societies recognized as abnormal epilepsy, mania, florid schizophrenia, acute confusion, marked dementia, agitation, and severe mental defect. There are even local names for a variety of mental afflictions, as Brelsford[42] and Leighton and Hughes[158] have shown. As to how many of these well-recognized types of case will be brought to the notice of authority and so to the medical officer or the psychiatrist is, however, very much a matter of local circumstance, since most cases are dealt with, in the first instance at least, by native "medicine-men". The cases the psychiatrist sees are, all too often, the failures of these latter. The present writer[50] showed that the average time from onset till admission in Kenya was $6\frac{1}{2}$ months, and Prince[210] has well described the highly developed indigenous psychiatry of western Nigeria.

The types of cases which are not often likely to be brought to the notice of official psychiatry in Africa include the high-grade defectives, simple schizophrenics, paranoiacs, retarded depressives, and indeed, all types of disturbance which do not impinge too alarmingly upon the community.

This takes one to the final difficulties—difficulties which concern the diagnosis and categorizing of the cases when the latter *are* seen.

Difficulties in history-taking and examination of the patient have been well summarized by Margetts[170]. Patients often arrive at mental hospitals unaccompanied by anyone who knows their history and in a mental state too disturbed to give a reliable history themselves. They may even have come from an area where the local language can hardly be interpreted at the hospital, but even if it can be reasonably well interpreted (as is the rule), the subtleties of language are likely to be lost. Few qualified African psychiatrists exist as yet and the European psychiatrist communicates with his patients through an interpreter or through some lingua franca of which Bateson[14] writing of Pidgin English, has said: "It appears that Pidgin is not a means whereby the White man communicates white thoughts, nor is it a means by which the Native communicates native thoughts. It is another world in which White man and Native meet. In this other world they feel that they communicate fully and richly, but the matter of their communication is not closely related to the system of life in which either of them grew up."

Apart from language difficulties as such, there are difficulties of expression even within the subject's own language since habits of introspection are lacking, and misunderstandings arise at times from a tendency to concretise without literal intention, as Vyncke[256] has stressed. African subjects often also withhold information because they are suspicious of the European psychiatrist or feel that the latter could never understand their problems. Finally, the African patient does not expect to have to give much information, for a doctor worth his salt divines the answers for himself.

In view of all this, it has recently become customary to suggest that only African psychiatrists are adequate to deal with African mental patients, and Simons,[231] for instance, writing of the need for field work, says: "The employment of African psychiatrists for this purpose would be invaluable, if not indispensable. They would combine, as few other practitioners can do, the required knowledge of medicine and psychiatry with an intimate knowledge of the people's physiognomy, language, and traits." Carstairs[55] has also emphasized the point, and has argued that a psychiatrist working in an alien culture has the same sort of difficulties that he has in dealing with another class within his own culture. The present writer, while accepting the manifest advantages of training psychiatrists from among the peoples they will later be treating, finds no ideal solution here either. Carstairs's argument is double-edged, for an African who has acquired the high degree of European education and sophistication that must antedate a psychiatric qualification has moved into a world whose difference from his life before is incomparably greater than the difference between, say, British social classes.

And so one comes to the final problem, the categorizing of the cases. Epidemiological surveys are concerned, not only with total incidences and prevalences, perhaps in relation to age, sex, and other factors, but with the different psychiatric categories. Articles on psychiatry in many parts of Africa have appeared in recent decades containing classifications of the cases seen. Some of the authors are British, some French, some African, and on the whole the titles are familiar ones. But there remains the greatest doubt as to how far the cases classified under each title by one writer are comparable with those classified under that title by another. Diagnostic criteria are seldom well defined. It is safe to say that there is no perfect uniformity, and the W.H.O. Expert Committee on Mental Health in its Eighth Report[261] said:

> "One of the basic requirements of epidemiology is a generally accepted system of statistical classification which allows data obtained by various investigators to be confidently compared. The lack of a common classification of mental disorders has repeatedly defeated attempts at comparing psychiatric observations and the results of treatment undertaken in various countries and even in various centres in the same country. Although a great deal of time and effort has been spent on seeking a generally acceptable system, no satisfactory solution has yet been reached."

In the African studies previously referred to one certainly meets difficulties arising from this. But the trouble goes even deeper. Most of the writers, trained in England or France, have roughly the same ideas about classification. But, being doctors before they were psychiatrists, they suffer from the medical urge to classify cases under familiar titles. Failure to do so is apt to be seen as a failure in oneself rather than as an intractability in the material. The classifications are often only too complete and make little or, occasionally, no allowance for this intractability.

Finally, one has to ask how far it is safe, in dealing with peoples of such grossly different cultural backgrounds as Europeans and rural Africans, to use the familiar titles at all. Is schizophrenia, for instance, the same condition as schizophrenia in Europe if the response to ECTs is so much more dramatic and the prognosis in general so much better than it is in Europe? Is depression the same sort of condition as depression in Europe if hypochondriacal complaints with an unhappy appearance are the only symptoms?

In general, therefore, it seems that attempts to assess *total* incidence or prevalence figures in Africa south of the Sahara, though probably entirely premature at present, are only to be considered seriously where field studies have been done as well as hospital studies; but that *relations* between figures within these totals (as for sex, age, and the various psychiatric categories) are of greater value, if one continually bears in mind the factors previously described that tend to disturb these relations.

In making this general assessment the present writer finds himself in the very good company of Biesheuvel[25] Odegard,[187] and Wittkower and Fried.[266]

And so to the data.

Total incidence

For the reasons given earlier, only field studies will be dealt with here. They are described in chronological order.

Cheneveau[58] described a medical survey undertaken in French Togoland in 1933. The township of Anécho, with a population of about 5,000, was surveyed and 20 insane people were found; a prevalence rate of 4 per 1,000. Several comments could be made about this figure, but perhaps the most important is that it is customary in West Africa for defectives, simple schizophrenics, and other chronic psychiatric subjects to drift from the countryside into the townships where they live as beggars. The rate obtained therefore is probably quite excessive and this underlines the need for psychiatric surveys to include a broad cross-section of the population—urban and rural.

The Mental Hospital Departmental Committee in its report on mental derangement in South Africa[250] referred to a psychiatric census made earlier that year of a native population of nearly 389,000 people resident in Zululand and Natal. 315 people had been found to be mentally disordered, or 0·8 per 1,000 population, not counting some already housed in institutions. The present writer has not been able to discover further details of this census, but the Committee itself considered that it had been made by competent people and that the figures could be accepted as correct.

The present writer[50] obtained, through the local chiefs and headmen, censuses of the insane in three areas of Kenya having a total population of 616,000 and of the defective in two of these areas having a total population of 571,000. In each case the numbers of patients from these areas who were in the Colony's mental hospital at the time were added to the census figures and the figures of 228 and 251 respectively were arrived at; thus representing prevalence rates of about 0·4 per 1,000 for each category. The major criticism of these figures is that they depended on lay African diagnoses of mental defect and insanity. As such, they are likely to have included all the more severe cases that gave rise to social problems but to have ignored many milder cases, on the lines described in the introduction. The figures are therefore to be regarded as minimal.

Tooth[245] conducted a psychiatric survey in four areas of the then northern Gold Coast. He not only personally examined many cases, but also obtained reports of other cases from chiefs and census enumerators in these areas. In a total population of 166,269 he saw 99 insane people himself, and a further 61 were reported by other enumerators. He said that the rate calculated from those examined by himself (0·60 per 1,000 population) might be regarded as a minimal figure; while that calculated from the total of those seen by himself and the enumerators (0·96 per 1,000 population) was probably nearer the true rate.

Baasher[12] made a study of the population of a village, Ishkeit, in Wadi Halfa, Sudan. The resident population at the time of his survey was 1,860 mostly farming people. As an operational criterion, a person was regarded as psychologically disturbed whenever there was emotional or behavioural disorder of such a degree that the person became socially incapacitated or found difficulty in working efficiently, or that his condition warranted treatment. Numbers of cases were not quoted in his article, but prevalence rates per 1,000 population were found to be: psychoneuroses 40·9; schizophrenia 7·0; depression 5·9; psychosomatic disorder 5·4; mental retardation 3·8. At one point in time 6·3 per cent of this community were suffering from one or other of these conditions.

Leighton and 5 others[159]; made a study of psychiatric disorder in the Yoruba tribe of Nigeria. This was based on a random selection of adults living in 15 villages and 1 town, and a non-random selection of mental patients of the local mental hospital. Over 3 months, data were collected on 262 villagers, 64 residents of Abeokuta (a town of approximately 80,000 inhabitants), and 59 mental patients. Their results are expressed in terms of prevalence of symptom patterns and not of cases—an approach which is only useful for comparison of sub-groups within the studied group or for comparison with observations similarly made elsewhere, such as those made previously by Leighton in Stirling County, Canada. They found, in general, that the Yoruba group seemed to have more symptoms (especially of psychophysiologic and psychoneurotic types) but fewer cases of clearly evident psychiatric disorder than Stirling County; but on the whole they were more impressed by the similarities, both of quality and prevalence, than by the differences.

Besides field studies concerned with the total prevalence of all forms of mental disturbance there have been a few in which the total prevalence of certain categories have been studied and, since these have an important bearing on total prevalence in general, this seems the proper place to mention them.

Field,[97] on the basis of information given by co-operative chiefs and elders, examined all the persons regarded by these as suffering from mental abnormality in 12 Ashanti country-towns and villages, representing a population estimated by the 1948 census at 4,283. She concentrated on schizophrenia and excluded from her prevalence assessment all those people who came from other areas, epileptics, late treated trypanosomiosis subjects, defectives, and all persons in whom the diagnosis remained in doubt. She found 41 cases: a prevalence rate of 0·95 per cent, corresponding to a figure in Europe and America of about 0·8 per cent to 1·0 per cent. Two comments are called for. Field's discovery of the cases was dependent on the recognition of the mentally sick by chiefs and elders, for she had found that Africans on the whole were shrewd at diagnosing insanity, and often knew the main differential diagnoses, and on several occasions even knew a subject was "becoming mad" better than she did herself. This is quite in accord with the present writer's experience. The second comment is that, if this part of Ashanti is anything like most other parts of Africa, a census made in 1948 would be a considerable under-estimate of the population in 1960. Allowing for this, however, and allowing for the probability that more cases were missed than would be missed in Europe, it would seem that the incidence of schizophrenia, in this part of Africa at least, is probably of a similar order to that found in Europe.

Piraux[204] took the opportunity, when 15,000 people in Ruanda-Urundi were called up for a medical census, to investigate the number of epileptics in that community. Although epilepsy as such is hardly a psychiatric concern, his study has an epidemiological interest for psychiatry that goes far beyond epilepsy, as will appear later. He found 68 cases, or a prevalence rate of 0·45 per cent. He states that "the real proportion of epileptics in the population is very likely higher than that figure, as these 68 cases were known to have severe convulsions frequently and we probably missed all the minor types of seizures". Here again, therefore, since the equivalent figure in Europe is also about 0·4 per cent, the incidence would seem to be of a similar order to that found in Europe.

As regards total incidence in general it is only clear that it would be quite premature as yet to make *any* firm assertions. The evidence is too meagre and too conflicting to say more than that the prevalence of mental disorder is probably not less than 1 per 1,000 and may well be considerably more.

Sex incidence

In all mental hospital figures in Africa men outnumber women by 2 or more to 1. Thus, in regard to in-patients at any one time in Nyasaland,[225] in the Gold Coast,[245] and in Nigeria,[46] the ratio was 6 to 1; in Tanganyika[233] and the Belgian Congo[165] it was about 3 to 1; in South Africa and excluding defectives[236] it was 2·5 to 1; and in Lagos[38] it was about 2 to 1. In regard to new admissions the ratio in South Africa, excluding defectives[236] was 2·6 to 1; and in Kenya[50] it was 1·9 to 1.

Since in mental hospitals in western Europe and America there are rather more women than men, both as in-patients and as admissions, one has to ask whether the sex discrepancy observed in African psychiatry corresponds to a real difference in sex incidence, or is wholly accounted for (as it certainly is in part) by the fact that women are more easily looked after at home and are in far greater proportion living at home in circumstances where they can be so looked after. The answer can only be found by turning to those field surveys that are helpful in regard to this question.

The present writer[50] in his rural survey in Kenya found a ratio of 1·5 male insane to 1 female. Tooth[245] in his rural survey in the Gold Coast found a ratio of 1·7 males to 1 female. Field[97] in her rural survey of chronic schizophrenia in Ghana found a ratio of roughly 1 male to 1 female.

Piraux's[204] field survey of epilepsy in Ruanda-Urundi took account of sex distribution. He had observed that 72 per cent of epileptics seen at hospital were males and he then investigated the number in the community on the basis of 15,000 persons, as described before. Among the 68 cases discovered, 45 were males and 23 females, a ratio of 2 to 1. He also recorded that there were slightly more women than men both in the general population of Ruanda-Urundi and in the out-patient clinics there. It is therefore clear, not only that there are far fewer female epileptics, but that the discrepancy observed in the field is not *much* less than that observed at the hospital. This point will be referred to again.

Field surveys of much value but which cannot be described in terms of "cases", have also been made in western Nigeria by Leighton and 5 others;[159] by D. Leighton;[160] and by Hughes.[128] Their results, in terms of prevalence of symptoms, however, (and apart from the effects of village distintegration which will be described in a later section of this chapter) go to show that on the whole the village women are mentally healthier than the men. This is due, the writers believe, to the fact that culture-change has affected the women to a lesser degree.

These are the data. What is to be made of them? On the

whole the evidence from field surveys supports the hospital observations, though to a lesser degree. In other words, there probably *is* a lesser incidence of severe psychiatric disorder among the women. Piraux's findings strike the present writer as particularly interesting in this connection, and perhaps partly because Piraux's concern is not directly with psychiatry. Nearly as large a proportion of the women as of the men who suffer from epilepsy come to hospital notice, the attendance proportion of the former being over three-quarters of that of the latter. One can see no good reason why a proportion of the same order should not apply in the case of severe psychiatric disorders. Thus, if the real incidence of these disorders were the same in the two sexes one would expect (on the basis of Piraux's experience) that the proportion of female psychiatric cases would be about three-quarters of that of the male. Yet the facts are otherwise, and one is led to infer that severe mental disorder is in fact of a lesser incidence among the women. Vyncke,[256] also working in Ruanda-Urundi, may well have hit the nail on the head when he wrote that psychoses are more common among the men, and neuroses among the women.

Most writers on the subject of sex incidence refers to the fact that the men are more directly faced with the problems of culture contact. Mairlot, for instance, records that whereas only 20 per cent of the men seen in the Belgian Congo seem to have had no contact with Western culture, 60 per cent of the women have had no such contact. This sort of difference of experience is almost universal in Africa, and is likely after all to have psychiatric implications.

Age incidence

The mean age on admission to hospital has been recorded as 35 years in Nyasaland;[225] 33 years in Kenya;[50] 32 years in Tanganyika[233] and, at onset of illness, 28 years in the Gold Coast[245]. Moreover, the present writer[52] found that 78 per cent of his Kenya patients were admitted between the ages of 10 and 40 years, the equivalent figure in the USA, being 42 per cent; and Lamont and Blignault[154] found that 94 per cent of their male Bantu admissions in South Africa were between the ages of 20 and 50 years.

Africans in the past have seldom known their age; their ages are estimated by the psychiatrist and usually under-estimated.

But, even allowing for this, the average age on first admission is much less than that found in first admissions in Europe and America.

The main reason for this is undoubtedly that the bulk of the population living away from home in circumstances where home care is difficult, or not available, are young adults. Other factors are the shorter expectation of life in Africa, and differences in the relative incidence of the several psychiatric categories, which will be discussed in later sections of this chapter.

Incidence in relation to acculturation

Psycho-somatic and organic conditions related to culture change will not be considered here. Much has also been written about the relation of particular categories of mental illness to various aspects of acculturation, but it is more appropriate to refer to this under the heading of the categories concerned.

The present writer,[50] in his Kenya Hospital material, recorded a certification rate of 2·3 per 100,000 of the rural population, and of 13·3 per 100,000 of the population employed or living away from home, and was particularly struck by the fact that the latter figure was still so low compared to the American figure (of 95 per 100,000) for the comparable age group there. He believed that these findings supported the contention that psychotic incidence was related to acculturation.

Tooth[245] has discussed this question on the basis of the numbers of affected near relatives of literate and non-literate psychotics in his Gold Coast survey. He found no evidence from his figures to support the hypothesis that psychosis is commoner in the Westernized group than in the rest of the population. He emphasized, however, that his survey could only go a small way towards answering the question as it took no account of neuroses and minor forms of personality disorder.

Smartt[233] recorded that only 9 per cent of the total African population of Tanganyika had attended school, yet 28 per cent of his hospital admisssions had done so. He made an enquiry, however, into the comparable rate among the admissions to 5 general hospitals in that country, found the rate was even higher (33 per cent), and concluded that the educated part of the population simply took greater advantage of the official medical and psychiatric facilities.

Vyncke,[256] in a psychiatric study in Ruanda-Urundi, found that psychiatric morbidity was high out of all proportion among Congo immigrants into Ruanda-Urundi. There were, in fact, 352 cases from an indigenous population of 4,000,000 (a rate of 9 per 100,000), and 157 cases from a Congolese immigrant population of not more than 20,000 (a rate of 785 per 100,000). He attributed this to the fact that the Congolese concerned had broken away from their ancestral customs, had emulated the Western way of life, and had thereby been subjected to much emotional tension and conflict. This may well be so, but it has also to be said that, with this background, they are much more likely than are the local rural people to avail themselves of the official psychiatric facilities. Vyncke[256] also found that neuroses, as opposed to psychoses, were twice as commonly seen in educated (instruits) or sophisticated (évolués) Africans as in others.

Leighton and 5 others[159] found that sociocultural disintegration in western Nigeria was accompanied by an increase in psychiatric symptoms, which was mainly accounted for by a marked increase of these symptoms among the women. In the villages which they assessed as "disintegrated" they even found a reversal of the usual relative sex incidence seen in African psychiatry (and seen in the Nigerian villages in general) to the degree that there were more symptoms among the women than among the men. They interpreted this finding on the lines that, for the women the "traditional sources of security are failing and are not yet replaced by functionally effective new patterns"; the situation in the case of the men being different in that the latter have for much longer been exposed to the turmoils of social change, an interpretation which the present writer finds entirely convincing. Their findings, in regard to the influence of education and literacy, pointed suggestively towards an association of these with an increase of psychiatric symptoms, but the figures were too small to permit of definite conclusions or tests of significance.

Finally, Fortes and Mayer[100] on the basis of a 2½-year study of the Tallensi of northern Ghana completed in 1937 and of a further three months contact in 1963, found a great increase in psychoses in the later period. In the first period only one psychotic subject was seen, whereas in the second 13 were seen, the great majority being schizophrenic. The writers discuss and rule out the possibilities that the increase was importantly related to population increase in the intervening period, or to the existence of other unseen psychotics or the early death of psychotics in the former period. They attribute the increase to the great social changes, in the direction of Westernization and loss of the traditional disciplines and values, which had manifestly occurred in Tallensi country in the intervening years.

In summary, apart from Fortes and Mayer's impressive observations, the findings are ambiguous and the present writer believes that attempts to discover how far cultural change influences total psychiatric incidence are neither likely to produce any simple overall answer nor figures that are very meaningful. Cultural change in the direction of Westernization is, however, certainly likely to alter the relative incidence of various psychiatric categories with the replacement of syndromes seen commonly in rural Africans by the neurotic and psychotic patterns familiar to European psychiatrists. Thus, it would seem to be more profitable to consider this problem in relation to the several psychiatric categories.

As evidence of the overall effects of acculturation, however, there does remain the striking disparity in sex incidence constantly observed in Africa. This disparity, which is probably in part a real one (see the earlier discussion of Piraux's findings), has no parallel in European psychiatric experience and may well be best explained by the effects of an acculturation which acts much more markedly at first upon the men, and only later on the women.

The Psychiatric Categories

Epidemiology of the major categories

This aspect of psychiatric epidemiology is, as indicated earlier, on rather surer ground than aspects concerned with total incidence.

There follows in tabular form a representative series of admission samples classified in the major categories as recorded by several authorities. Ideally, the cases would be categorized in terms of, say, the W.H.O. International Classification of Diseases. This, however, is not at present possible, for the available figures have not been presented in that form. The figures are expressed as percentages of total admissions and, with one exception, are shown to the nearest whole number, since diagnostic and other criteria do not warrant assessments at a higher level of exactitude. Neuroses are not included in this table since large numbers of such cases were seen at a few institutions and few or none at others, thus vitiating the other proportions. The latter have been scaled independently. Cases in which no mental illness was found have also been excluded. The South African Annual Report figures do not include a heading for "unclassified psychoses" but do include one for "other psychoses" so that, partly for tabular convenience, the latter cases are here included under the former heading. The last two columns show, for comparison, figures for American Negroes of the State of Massachusetts and for South African Whites.

The high figure for mental defect in the last column merely reflects the fact that the South African Annual Report included figures for persons housed in institutions for White defectives, whereas no such institutions for African defectives as such existed at that time, either in South Africa or in the rest of Africa south of the Sahara.

It can be seen that there is a considerable variation from column to column and a striking variation from all the others in the 6th column: a matter which will be discussed in later pages.

Organic psychoses

Much that is relevant to these psychoses has already been described in chapters 3 and 4.

The proportion of organic psychoses among admission figures in Africa is always quite high, averaging 28 per cent in the tabulated samples. The infective-exhaustive psychoses play a large part; constituting about a quarter of the organic psychoses in several available series. Common throughout the continent as causative agents are malaria, pneumonia, and puerperal and septic conditions. Collomb and Massat[69] find that schistosomiasis can be complicated by a variety of neuro-psychiatric manifestations, though their frequency is difficult to assess. Trypanosomiasis is endemic in West Africa and a common cause of mental disturbance there (24 out of 32 organic psychoses seen by Tooth[245] in the Gold Coast). As regards the symptomatology, classical confusional states are common, but schizophrenic syndromes are also common and this is true not

	Gordon, 1936[119] 120 Male Cases, Kenya	Carothers, 1947[50] 558 Cases, Kenya	Lamont and Blignault, 1953[154] 257 Male Cases, South Africa	Smartt, 1956[233] 232 Cases, Tanganyika	Vyncke, 1957[255] 355 Cases, Ruanda-Urundi	Tewfik, 1958[243] 304 Cases, Uganda	Lambo, 1960[151] 3,975 Cases, Nigeria	Collomb, 1965[65] 2,000 Cases, Senegal	South African Annual Report for 1960[236]; 2,041 Cases	Dayton, 1940[79] American Negroes; Average of 78 Cases per annum	South African Annual Report for 1960;[236] 999 European Cases
Organic Psychoses	44	33	34	26	32	11	17	} 21	20	47	31
Epileptic Psychoses	6	4	6	10	16	3	9	}	8	3	5
Mental Defect	15	12	3	3	4	1	3	—	3	4	25
Psychopathy	—	3	—	—	1	—	2	—	—	1	—
Schizophrenia-Paranoia	25	31	54	27	18	(0.3)	40	21	58	31	22
Affective Disorder	2	5	3	20	18	3	15	21	6	9	9
Unclassified Psychoses	8	11	—	14	10	82	13	37	4	5	7

The figure 37 at the bottom of column 8 comprises "bouffées délirantes" (six-sevenths) and "etats confusionnels" (one-seventh).

only of trypanosomiasis (as shown by Tooth) but also in tropical neuropathy (as shown by Asuni[8]), and in other organic settings.

Syphilis plays a large, but apparently decreasing, part in psychiatry in many areas of Africa—East, West, and South—constituting about one quarter of the organic psychoses in available admission figures; but seems not to be so common in Nigeria (Lambo[151]) and Ruanda-Urundi (Vyncke[255]). Clinically, general paralysis and meningo-vascular syphilis are its chief forms, while tabes is rare.

Senile and arteriosclotic psychoses play a much smaller part in African than in European psychiatry, accounting for only about one-seventh of the admissions of organic psychoses in the available figures. This is probably accounted for, partly by the fact that the expectation of life in general is less; partly in that there is a far better place for the elderly and aged in African rural life than there is in urban Europe; and partly by the general rarity of atherosclerotic cerebral thrombosis, though it seems that this is no longer true of certain urban areas, as shown by Collomb[65] for Dakar.

In regard to drugs, alcohol is much less of a psychiatric problem on the whole in Negroes than it is in Whites in Africa, since the consumption of spirits is largely confined to townships. The excessive consumption of alcohol in other forms is, however, a potent source of crime, as was shown in Chapter 4. Indian Hemp (Cannabis sativa) is increasingly consumed in some areas, notably in Lagos (Boroffka[37]) and Dakar (Collomb et al.[68]), and Boroffka has shown that, of the 224 subjects admitted to the mental hospital at Lagos over a 4-year period with a history of hemp taking, about half were diagnosed as suffering from a toxic psychosis. Miraa (Catha edulis) is frequently chewed in East Africa, and this also may lead to mental disturbance, as shown by the present writer,[49] and by Margetts.[173]

Other organic psychoses include those caused by malnutrition, a variety of encephalites and encephalopathies, and by cerebral tumours.

Epilepsy

Epilepsy is common throughout Africa and accounts for about 8 per cent of the admissions to mental hospitals. It has been described on much the same lines in East Africa,[1, 50, 234, 225]; in West Africa,[11, 64]; and in South Africa.[154] One is fortunate in being able to record prevalence rates for this illness which are probably near the mark of: 0·45 per cent among 15,000 people of Ruanda-Urundi (Piraux[204]); 0·21 per cent among 10,000 persons in Uganda (Orley[191]); 2·01 per cent among 10,000 Wapogoro of Tanzania (Jilek and Jilek-Aall).[139]

Few cases are due to cysticercosis. Thus Gelfand[112] found it only 7 times in 2,148 autopsies in Rhodesia, and Lambo[153] only saw 5 cases in a 9-year period in Nigeria. The part played by other infections remains an open question, but it is of interest to record that only 16 per cent of Piraux' cases were definable as "idiopathic" in the sense that no lesion was discoverable by radiological or other procedures, and that a higher proportion of his cases was associated with atrophic cerebral lesions than has been found in Europe or America.

Clinically, epileptics show the same symptoms and psychiatric syndromes as in Europe. Schizophrenia—like psychoses in persons suffering from epilepsy have sometimes been observed in Europe (Slater *et al.*,[232]) and Asuni and Pillutla[10] observed that 11 out of a total of 42 epileptic patients studied in Nigeria exhibited schizophrenic symptoms.

Those epileptics who are admitted to mental hospitals are usually demented or anti-social, and the great majority have serious burn scars due to having fallen into the unguarded fire at some time—a useful distinction from hysteria. Epileptics in Africa are the most unfortunate of people, shunned by all in the belief that their condition is contagious, and with an urge to be cured which must drive most of them sooner or later, to apply for official medical help.

Mental defect

Mental defect, usually with psychosis, accounts for about 5 per cent of admissions to institutions in Africa. This low figure, however, is mainly a measure of the lack of official accommodation for African defectives, as is well seen in the great discrepancy between the figures for Whites and Bantus in South Africa.

The present writer found, in a series of 100 people charged with homicide in Kenya, that 8 were mentally deficient; while, among the 57 psychiatric homicidal patients in the mental hospital at Nairobi on one day in 1949, no less than 14 (or 24.6 per cent) were feeble-minded persons; this figure might be compared with that given by Norwood East 86, which was 16 (or 5.3 per cent) mentally deficient subjects among 300 Broadmoor homicides. These figures simply serve to remind one that, whereas in western Europe a high proportion of the defective population is under some sort of official care or supervision (and thus prevented from committing crime), in rural Africa this is not so.

In fact, as Collomb[65] has also emphasized, such people are wonderfully well tolerated within the community in Africa. But, apart from this in rural societies where conformity and lack of initiative are esteemed, mental defect in its higher grades is by no means so discernible as it becomes in urban and industrial life and particularly when literacy becomes general.

Of the special types, congenital syphilis with mental defect, microcephaly, cretinism, and congenital diplegia were seen by the present writer;[50] epiloia and bilateral athetosis by Smartt;[233]

gargoylism by Stephens;[239] and 103 cases of infantile hydroce-
phalus were treated in Nairobi over a 7-year period as described
by Chauhan.[57] It is, however, the universal experience throughout Africa that mongolism is rare, though it has now been
described by Luder and Musoke[162] in Uganda, and by Leather
and Leather[157] also in Uganda. This accords with American
experience, since Malzberg[169] found that the rate in American
Negroes was only about one-third of that for Whites, and
Jarvis,[136] judging from the incidence in institutions, found it to
be 10 times less frequent in American Negroes than in American
Whites.

Psychopathic states

Psychopathic states account for only about 1 per cent of
admissions to mental hospitals in Africa.

What constitutes a "case" in regard to these states is so
dependent on the attitude of the community and on the degree
of asocial or even antisocial behaviour which the latter is prepared
to tolerate, that attempts to assess the size of this problem on
epidemiological lines are rather meaningless. Thus inadequate
and ineffectual people can easily "get by" in rural Africa, as
Field[97] has shown in Ghana; and episodic aggression is sometimes
an expected pattern of behaviour, as will be seen when the
unclassified cases are discussed.

The present writer, in an early article,[51] wrote that if psychopathic persons can be defined as those "who live in a perpetual
here-now and lack the desire or ability to control their passing
emotions and so to subordinate immediate gratification to their
own long-term interests" (and having regard to the common
occurrence of "frenzied anxiety" among persons who appear
after the storm has passed to be perfectly normal Africans) then
"the resemblance between the mentality of the normal primitive
African and a certain type of aberrant European mentality commonly included under the title psychopathic is found to be very
close".

It has, however, to be clearly stated at this point that this
finding was based on a series of examples of irresponsible
behaviour committed by Africans in their working relationships
with Europeans; in situations where their own codes of
behaviour were no longer applicable and where the alien codes
were strange. *They occurred*, in other words, in a *highly transitional*

and rather meaningless world. The title "psychopathic", in its only valuable usage has antisocial connotations, and the application of this title to people who, in indigenous life, are supremely well integrated into their society, is clearly a mis-usage.

It is, however, equally clear, as was indicated in an earlier chapter, that the indigenous cultural modes prepare a man but poorly for life in a world of change. It is therefore to be expected that psychopathic states will be seen increasingly, and this is borne out by Dembovitz'[82] observation of the frequent need to repatriate West African soldiers on account of psychopathic personality, and by Lambo's[151] finding, in psychiatric patients admitted to Aro Hospital, Nigeria, that among 948 patients from rural areas there was only one such case (0·1 per cent), whereas among 3,027 patients from urban areas there were 38 (1·3 per cent).

Schizophrenia-paranoia

Schizophrenia accounted for an average of 28 per cent of the admission figures in the tabulated samples, or 31 per cent if one excludes Tewfik's figure. Most psychiatric observers throughout Africa have found this illness to be a common, if not the commonest, type of mental disturbance in Africans. Tewfik's divergent views will be considered later.

Field's[97] survey in Ashanti land, already recorded and commented upon, showed that the prevalence of schizophrenia there was of roughly the same order of magnitude as that found in Europe and America.

Typical cases of each of the commonly recognized subcategories—simple, hebephrenic, catatonic and paranoid— have been reported by most observers, and figures for each have often been recorded in hospital admissions.

In regard to paranoid types of schizophrenia, persecutory delusions are the rule and grandiose are rare. It seems, moreover, that paranoid patients from rural areas rarely, if ever, show the well organized delusional systems that characterize the paraphrenic or paranoiac cases seen in western Europe, though they do occur in urban literate Africans. This has been described by Aubin[11] in West Africa; the present writer[51] in East Africa; Collomb[65] in Senegal; and Lambo[149] in Nigeria.

Apart from cases that fit fairly easily into the classical European text-book categories, schizophrenia in Africans is often very amorphous clinically, and marked above all by excitement and a confusional mental state which is more like that seen in organic conditions in Europe. This fact has been emphasized by Forster[99] in Ghana; Gillis[115] in South Africa; Lambo[149] in Nigeria; Laubscher[155] in South Africa; Smartt[233] in Tanzania, and Tooth[245] in the Gold Coast. Moreover, Wittkower *et al.*,[267] in their cross-cultural enquiry into the symptomatology of schizophrenia, found a relatively high frequency of visual and tactile hallucinations in Africans (and Arabians). Several writers (Berman,[18] Fortes and Mayer,[100] Lambo,[151] and Lamont and Blignault[154] have found that schizophrenia in Africans carries a better prognosis, responds better to electro-convulsive treatment, and is less subject to recurrence than in Europeans; findings which are well supported by the South African mental hospital figures (Annual Report 1960) for, whereas among South African Whites the proportion of schizophrenics among the resident mental hospital population is 52 per cent greater than the proportion among the admission cases, the equivalent figure for South African Bantu is only 21 per cent.

So striking indeed are these differences that Tewfik[243] has even questioned the validity of the diagnosis of schizophrenia as made by other psychiatrists in Africa. In a series of 304 African admissions to the mental hospital of Uganda and using "strict diagnostic criteria", he only diagnosed this condition in 1 case and relegated as many as 247 patients to his "unclassified group". While the present writer believes that Tewfik's diagnostic strictness goes much too far, he also believes that his approach does raise important issues. Although schizophrenia does, in his view and in that of most other writers, occur in Africans in classical forms and by no means so uncommonly, there is also no doubt that this title has often been used as a dumping ground on to which many cases—which did not fit into other clinical categories—have been relegated.

Much of the difficulty in regard to the epidemiology of schizophrenia stems from the fact that the word is used in two senses. Sometimes it is used simply to describe certain clinical syndromes without other implications; at other times it is seen as an illness with implications in regard to aetiology and prognosis. In the present very uncertain state of knowledge of the causation of the clinical syndromes entitled schizophrenic, one can only say that the African evidence seems to support the contention that there *is* a genetic tendency to schizophrenic illness, characterized at its minimum by a loss of alert rapport with the outer world, and which may be of roughly the same order of frequency in Africa as in Europe; but that in rural non-literate Africans it takes clinical forms which are often amorphous or confusional rather than of the classical European patterns.

The part played by literacy in this jigsaw puzzle is important and may provide part of the key to its understanding. Gordon[119] held, not only that all his schizophrenics were literate, but that all his literate admissions were schizophrenic. Field[96] found that, although the general rate of literacy in Ghana as usually estimated was only 10 per cent, the literacy rate among her schizophrenic cases was over 40 per cent, and explained this disparity on the grounds that life for the rural non-literate Ghanaian was exceedingly simple, whereas for the literate (even living within Ghana) it was a battle. Thus, first, simple schizophrenics can pass unnoticed in the rural community and, secondly, other potential schizophrenics may never meet the triggering stress in that community. It may also be that, since it is only, or mainly, literate schizophrenics who develop the classical pictures, it is sometimes, as with Gordon, only these who are so diagnosed.

The absence of systematization in the rural cases is no doubt partly to be accounted for on the lines that the African finds little need to rationalize his persecutory ideas since "evil willing" by others (from the material or the spiritual world) is part of his cultural heritage and is as implicitly assumed by his neighbours as it is by himself. But the present writer believes that all the differences mentioned above are to be seen as an outcome of something much deeper and more general than this—the fact, described in the chapter on psychology, that integration in African life is social rather than personal.

It is often said, as it was by Laubscher,[155] that the cultural background determines the nature of the mental content (delusional details, etc.) in this illness, but does not affect its structure as compared with the structure seen in schizophrenics in, say, Europe. But, unless one assumes, with Tewfik,[243] that schizophrenia is much rarer than it is elsewhere, it would seem that the structure also is determined by the cultural background.

Affective Disorder

Affective disorder accounted for an average of 9 per cent of the admissions in the tabular series of admission samples.

It played, almost consistently throughout that series, a much smaller part than schizophrenia, and it plays a still smaller part (as in Europe) among the cases in hospitals at any particular time. The various types of mania and depression will be discussed in this section, and suicide will also be discussed in view of its particular relevance to depression and its significance for the latter's epidemiology.

1 Mania

Most psychiatric writers who have recorded figures for mania and depression separately among their hospital patients, either as admissions or as in-patients[50, 119, 154, 165, 180, 233, 243] recorded manic cases more commonly than depressive. Tooth,[245] in a rural survey in the Gold Coast, had a similar experience. Aubin,[11] Collomb,[65] and Field,[97] on the other hand, observed depressive cases more frequently than manic. These divergent findings will be discussed under the heading of depression.

Hypomanic and acute manic patients, with the classical clinical features of these conditions, are quite commonly seen, though grandiose scheming is seldom a feature and elation is often ill-sustained. A large proportion of these classical cases are seen in persons with some European education or sophistication, a point remarked upon by Aubin,[11] Tewfik,[243] and the present writer.[51] Several writers have also observed a marked tendency to recurrence in their more typical manic patients, and others have noted a relatively high frequency of chronic mania, as compared with European figures.

Apart from these more typical cases, however, other cases occur, and not uncommonly, with super-added schizophrenic features, especially bizarre exaggerated movements and facial expressions, or with confusional features, and it is relevant here to quote a penetrating observation by Lambo[151] in regard to Nigerian psychiatric patients in general. He wrote that "most psychoses showed a moderate to a marked degree of excitement with little or no prognostic or diagnostic significance . . . the 'excitement syndrome' in one or another form may be the most striking, if not the only manifestation of an attack of psychosis, which remits spontaneously, leaving the clinician in a dilemma". This is an important observation which may well be true throughout Africa south of the Sahara. This non-specific excitement has not been sufficiently recognized in the past and this is likely to have given rise to some overloading of the category of mania.

In regard, therefore, to the epidemiology of mania in general, it has to be said, first, that the figures, as recorded, have often probably been too high due to the ubiquity of this excitomotor syndrome. And secondly, it has to be said that classical cases are also not uncommon throughout Africa; but since acute mania is a dramatic disturbance, a larger proportion of the cases are likely to be brought to hospitals than is likely with some other categories of psychosis, and that this is particularly true if, as with chronic mania, the condition is long-lasting.

2 Depression

Many psychiatric writers have commented on the rarity of depression in Africans. Thus Gordon[119] saw none in Kenya in a series of 120 admissions; Lamont and Blignault[154] saw 3 cases in South Africa in 258 admissions; Mairlot[165] saw only 1 case of typical melancholia in 100 inpatients in the Congo; Moffson[180] saw only 2 cases in 400 admissions in South Africa; Smartt[233] saw 15 cases in Tanganyika in 252 admissions; Tewfik[243] saw 3 cases in Uganda in 304 admissions; and the present writer[51] saw 24 cases in Kenya in 1508 admissions. The average of all these is only about 2 per cent of the admissions, yet at least one of the writers, Tewfik—as well as the present writer—also dealt with European patients and diagnosed depression in the latter very frequently.

Other writers have not found depression so rare. Thus Collomb and Zwingelstein[70] diagnosed this condition in 16·3 per cent of a series of 580 psychiatric admissions at Dakar; and Prince[212] saw 7 depressives in 101 patients studied at psychiatric treatment centres in Nigeria. Aubin[11] and Field[97] have, without giving figures, remarked upon the frequency of depression in Africans. Leighton and 5 others[159] found psychoneurotic depressive symptoms more commonly, and psychotic depressive symptoms less commonly, in the Nigerian than in the Stirling County groups they studied.

These divergencies might have been related to a varying incidence in different parts of Africa. No doubt this played some part, but the present writer sees no reason to believe that this was an important part. Tooth[245] and Field,[97] for instance, were both engaged in field studies in Ghana, yet Tooth only saw 6 depressives among 173 mentally disordered persons (3·5 per cent), whereas Field wrote that "Depression is the commonest mental illness of Akan rural women". In fact, when one studies the writings of the several authorities in detail, it becomes only too clear that the problem hinges on criteria of diagnosis.

Depression or melancholia, in its classical forms, characterized by deep depression, with either retardation or agitation, with ideas of unworthiness, guilt, remorse, hopelessness, or nihilistic delusions is, according to the great majority of writers, rare in rural Africans. Involutional depression in classical forms is also generally found to be rare, a fact which Collomb[65] relates to the full acceptance of and the respect accorded to the elderly in African society. In so far, therefore, as depressions of the fully-fledged European psychotic types are seen at all in Africans, they are mostly seen in the Westernized (the évolués)—the urbanized literate sections of the population.

Not infrequently, however, other patients are seen who appear to be sad and who complain of a variety of bodily ills; and others again who, with these symptoms, are also confused, or persecutory in the sense that they believe their sick condition is due to bewitchment. Yet these people have no discoverable physical illness and do not admit to depression. These cases have been described by Collomb and Zwingelstein[70] Collomb,[65] Gillis,[115] Lambo,[150, 151] Smartt,[233] and by the present writer[51, 52] who has also drawn attention to the fact that Africans with mania admit to elation quite readily, and that if depression were *felt*, it would surely be admitted *more* readily by people who are in general averse to admitting success. How far cases such as these are to be placed in a psychotic rather than in some neurotic category remains, however, very unclear. They respond well to ECT's, but so do many Africans with schizophrenic symptoms, so this also hardly clarifies the situation.

There remains one writer only who has maintained that depression in all its classical forms is common in a rural African population. Field[97] wrote: "Depression is the commonest mental illness of Akan rural women and nearly all such patients come to the shrines with spontaneous self-accusations of witchcraft—that is of having caused harm without concrete act or conscious will." Of involutional depression, she said: "In rural Ghana, involutional depression with agitation is (as in our own society) one of the commonest and most clearly defined of mental illnesses."

Field's findings have been subjected to a very penetrating assessment by Prince[211] who, working in Nigeria, had been struck, like most earlier observers, by the rarity in Africa of "profoundly depressed, agitated, self-accusatory melancholics", and by the frequency of the hypochondriac cases that might or might not be included under the title "depressive". He was therefore surprised by Field's findings and made the point that a certain pattern of confession was an essential part of the "healing shrine" ritual in Ghana, not only for mental illness but for any other sort of illness. He said: "It is possible that many of Field's melancholics are similar in their basic structure to the 'depressives' reported in other parts of Africa (somatic complaint syndromes with unhappy faces) but that the self-accusations are situation determined additions giving them a pseudo-European flavour". The present writer believes that Prince's explanation is the correct one. There is no doubt that *if* rural Africans, anywhere in Africa, suffered from the profoundly depressed, agitated, self-accusatory type of melancholia, their self-accusations would often take the form of having bewitched their relations on the lines described by Field. Yet, in the African depressives who do arrive at hospitals in Africa, this development is conspicuously lacking.

In general it is noteworthy that it is the later writers who have described depression as common, but that they have used this title in a much broader sense than the earlier writers. Prince,[212] in a thought-provoking article to which full justice cannot be done here, relates the change in diagnostic fashion to the move from the Colonial era to the era of Independence—a move which started (in Ghana) in 1957. He relates it particularly to 4 factors:

(1) The Prestige Factor; whereby, due to a belief, deep-rooted in Europeans, that it is only responsible people with a well-developed conscience who are subject to depression, this diagnosis only became appropriate for Africans in the era of Independence; the observing psychiatrists of each period being influenced by the climate of opinion of their time.

(2) The concept of Masked Depression; whereby, in the earlier period people complaining of a variety of bodily ills but not of depression were not included under that heading.

(3) The Alteration in Observational Setting; whereby depressive cases are unlikely to be admitted to the custodial type of mental hospital where most of the older observations were made,

whereas recent observations have also been made in out-patient clinics, rural surveys, etc.

(4) A True Alteration in Disease Pattern; whereby severe depressives do in fact occur more frequently with Westernization.

In comment on Prince's article, the present writer believes that all these factors have played some part, and that the second and third have surely played a large one, though he continues to question whether "depression" in the absence of all the severer symptoms (including suicide) should really be included in the same psychotic category as the severer forms that are commonly seen in Europe. As regards the fourth factor, he believes that this also is true and that the severe self-castigating types of depression are becoming increasingly common in Westernized Africans; in which belief he finds himself in the very good company of Asuni,[7, 9] and Collomb.[67]

The present writer would also take this opportunity to add a fifth factor; the influence on diagnosis of electro-convulsive treatment. This treatment emerged late in the Colonial period; it is much used—often very effectively—in a variety of psychiatric conditions in Africa and, when the patient improves, it is customary to assume that the condition that was cured was a depressive one. He believes that much of the recent increase in the diagnosis of depression has also been due to this, but questions its validity. Unless one is deeply committed to a faith, based on experience in Europe, that the therapeutic value of E.C. Treatment is uniquely related to depressive states and syndromes, a post-hoc diagnosis of depression following cure by this treatment is merely likely further to confuse the diagnostic issue in Africa.

Finally, it seems that the rarity or absence of profound self-castigating depressions in African rural life are to be seen as an outcome of a culture in which responsibility is communal rather than personal, on the lines described before. One aspect of this has been well described by Prince[209] in an article on cultural mechanisms for the mastery of grief among the Yoruba; and in general it would seem that, as with schizophrenia, the structure as well as the content of depression is determined by the cultural background.

3 Suicide

In a country like Africa where epidemiology is in its infancy, it is valuable to turn to such a theme as suicide which, with its legal repercussions, lends itself to this sort of study.

Most psychiatrists have observed that suicide was rare in Africans. Thus Berman[18] said of South Africa that the suicide rate was high in Whites, low in Coloured, and almost non-existent in the Bantu; and Lambo[150] said it was rare in primitive but not uncommon in Westernized Africans, and that a survey of 9 villages in Nigeria showed that, as far back as the elders could remember, no case had ever been reported or suspected.

The present writer,[51] in an indirect approach to the problem, and in view of the fact that many British homicides are depressive, and that in England 38 per cent of suspected murderers commit suicide before arrest, instituted an enquiry on this point in 5 districts in Kenya for the year 1946. He found that among 56 Africans suspected of murder, none committed suicide before arrest.

Laubscher[155] instituted an enquiry through the magistrates in certain native territories of South Africa and found in an area containing a population of 868,944 that there had been 14 suicides in a 2-year period; a rate of 0·8 per 100,000.

Bohannan[35] in a study of homicide and suicide among several tribes of Nigeria, Uganda, and Kenya found that "suicide rates in Africa would seem, on the basis of our data, to vary from moderate to low, but except for the Uganda tribes, the rates are not computable in a way that makes them comparable with those of the record-keeping world". In the 3 tribes in which the rates were computable—the Busoga, the Bunyoro, the Alur—the incidences work out at 7·0, 5·5, and 2·4 per 100,000 respectively, the average ages were 40 years, and the sex ratio about 2 male to 1 female.

Collomb, Zwingelstein, and Picca[71] found, by reference to the Courts at Dakar, that in the 7-year period 1955 to 1961, there had been 7 African suicides (all men), a rate of 1·4 for 100,000 of the African population; whereas there had been 6 European suicides (2 men and 4 women), a rate of 15 per 100,000 of the European population.

Sow[237] made a study, through all the official sources, of suicide in Senegal over a 2-year period and found there had been 47 suicides in this period in a population of approximately 3 million; a rate of 0·8 per 100,000 per annum. The male–female ratio was about 2 to 1, and the average age of the subjects was 39 years.

Asuni[6] made a study of suicide in western Nigeria, based on coroners' reports over the 4-year period 1957 to 1960. He considered it likely that most of the cases had been reported since fear of a later criminal charge would surely result from failure to do so. There was an average of 46·5 cases per year in a population of 6¾ million; a rate of about 0·7 per 100,000 per annum. The sex ratio was 3·65 men to 1 woman, and about as many persons committed suicide below the age of 50 years as above this age in terms of the rate for the population at risk.

With the exception of some of Bohannan's findings, there is thus a striking correspondence between those from various parts of Africa, and the figure, of about 1 per 100,000 per annum is much lower than the lowest recorded in Europe—that of Eire which was 2 per 100,000 in 1954. The sex ratio is nearly the same as that for the rest of the world, which is about 3 males to 1 female; while the average age at which the act is committed is much lower than in western Europe.

Apart from the recorded cases, there are two behaviour patterns, peculiar to Africa, which might be regarded as suicidal equivalents and which are unlikely to appear in the records First, wandering into the bush occurs from time to time in West African experience, as mentioned by Asuni.[7] Such people may not re-emerge but, if they do, they are in Asuni's words "in a sorry state of nutrition". They might perhaps best be regarded as attempted suicide equivalents. Second, "psycho-somatic death"—where the patient dies for no clear physical reason—probably occurs from time to time in Africans who believe their death is imminent. It is seldom reported, though Collomb has described a convincing case which was shortly reported in the Transcultural Psychiatric Research Review of October 1964.

In general, however, and in view of the fact that the severer types of depression carry a grave risk of suicide in Europe, the findings described above strongly support the contention that psychotic depressions are not only rare in mental hospitals in Africa but also in the general population.

Psychoneuroses

Psychoneuroses will be discussed in this section only in so far as they fit fairly readily into the classical clinical patterns seen in western Europe, with the addition of a syndrome (the brain-fag syndrome) which is also to be seen as psychoneurotic.

Neurotic patients are, in the present relatively undeveloped state of African psychiatric services, seldom admitted to mental hospitals. They are much more often seen, either as in-patients or out-patients at general hospitals or, as out-patients, at those few mental hospitals that have well-developed out-patient clinics or day accommodation.

Psychoneuroses in general are certainly common. Thus, among the 123 psychiatric cases described by Field[97] in rural Ghana, at least 21 were psychoneurotic; among the 2,724 psychiatric patients seen by Jakovljevic[135] in Guinea, 38 per cent were considered to be psychoneurotic; among the 3,975 psychiatric patients treated by Lambo[151] at Aro hospital in Nigeria, 1,578 were psychoneurotic; and among the 509 psychiatric patients seen by Vyncke[255] in Ruanda-Urundi, 123 were psychoneurotic. Lambo[151] has estimated that more than half the out-patients seen at general hospitals in most African countries, and three-quarters of those seen at native treatment centres in West Africa, are suffering from psychoneuroses.

Anxiety neuroses have been frequently observed, as by Collomb,[64, 65] Field,[97] Lambo,[150, 151] and Vyncke.[255] Cardiovascular or gastro-intestinal symptoms, headaches and impotence are probably the chief somatic manifestations. Lambo[151] says that anxiety neurosis is the commonest chronic emotional disturbance in students, the detribalized and the urbanized, whereas in rural non-literate people anxiety is more acute and takes other than classical forms. Smartt[233] makes the valuable observation that mild anxiety states with palpitations, precordial pain, and shortness of breath are seen at general hospitals, but that "severe anxiety states in pure culture are very rare, in fact, so rare that one might speculate on the possibility that other, maybe psychotic, reactions take the place of anxiety in African psychiatry".

Hysteria is very common, and this has been recorded by most observers, as by Collomb,[64, 65] Lambo,[150, 151] Muwazi and Trowell,[185] Smartt,[233] Verhaegen,[251] and Vyncke.[255] Lambo[151] found that a much greater proportion of his hysterical patients came from urban than from rural communities, but that whereas in the former monosymptomatic forms, such as paralyses, paraesthesiae, anaesthesiae, aphonia or deafness predominated, in the latter, massive disabilities predominated. Hysterical fits and stupors, and pseudocyesis are all common. As is the case in other parts of the world, hysteria is particularly frequent in African military personnel, as shown by Dembovitz.[82] Of the rarer hysterical manifestations, a case of Ganser syndrome and two cases of Camptocormie (a functional bent back in which the posture of advanced spondylitis deformans is assumed) have been seen and fully described in East Africans by Margetts.[172, 171]

An outbreak of mass hysteria in Uganda is described by Kagwa,[140] who also refers to two other outbreaks in East Africa, all 3 having occurred within a year of each other. Kagwa believes that these events arose out of the conflicts engendered by the great transition in Africa and sees a clear parallel with the mass hysterias which broke out towards the end of the Middle Ages in Europe.

Obsessional neuroses are distinctly rare, and Smartt[233] and the present writer[50] saw no such cases in their long series of psychiatric admissions in Tanganyika and Kenya. A few cases have, however, been described by Field,[97] Gordon,[119] Lambo,[150] Tooth[245] and Vyncke.[255]

Fears that would be described as phobias in a European setting abound in Africa, but are so much a part of the normal cultural and psychological setting here that the title "phobia" is inapplicable to these; and it would indeed be far from easy, at least for a non-African psychiatrist to distinguish a pathologically phobic case against this background.

In recent years there has emerged a neurosis which has been entitled the "brain-fag syndrome". It has been fully described by Prince [209] and afflicts particularly males between the ages of 15 and 30 years. It is very common in the student population of east and west Nigeria affecting 54 per cent of 844 students in one study (Savage and Prince[222]) and 35 out of 66 psychoneurotics seen in one year at Lagos (Boroffka and Marinho[39]). It may well have been seen but not distinguished under this title elsewhere, and some of Jakovljevic's psychoneurotics in Guinea, for instance, were probably of this category.

The onset is gradual with aching or burning sensations in the head and neck, and this is followed by disturbance of intellectual faculties (attention, concentration, and recall) and sensory functions, particularly visual. Thus the subject complains of inability to read, or to grasp or recall what is read, and may even complain that he cannot see the page or that his eyes are dazzled or that his sight is dim. He may also complain of an inability to write, and develop a weakness or shakiness of the right arm. Depression is rarely a complaint, but is occasionally severe. All the symptoms, at least at first, are confined to the educational working situation.

In discussing the aetiology of this condition, Prince[209] writes:

> "It is felt that the syndrome is not directly related to genetic factors, intelligence, parental literacy, study habits or family responsibilities. The hypothesis is presented that the syndrome is in some way related to the imposition of European learning techniques upon the Nigerian personality. It is suggested that European learning techniques emphasize isolated endeavour, individual responsibility, and orderliness—activities and traits which are foreign to the Nigerian by reason of the collectivistic society from which he derives, with heightened 'orality' and permissiveness."

The present writer finds this explanation entirely acceptable and would indeed see this syndrome as an expression of a subconscious antagonism to the written word and all it stands for by a society in transition from an "ear" to an "eye" culture, as described in the chapter on psychology.

Unclassified psychoses

Unclassified psychoses accounted for 18 per cent of the admissions in the tabulated series, or 9 per cent if one excludes Tewfik's figures.

The high figures for these psychoses recorded by most writers in African psychiatry are partly accounted for by language difficulties, lack of histories, and the other factors described in the introduction to this chapter. This, however, is by no means the whole story, for there still remain a large number of cases which do not fit into the familiar European categories. It is often even difficult to define particular cases as being neurotic or psychotic, as Collomb,[65] for one, has emphasized.

A large proportion of the unclassified cases show a clinical picture which was described by the present writer[50] under the title of "frenzied anxiety" in the following terms:

> "In this condition the onset is associated with some real source of anxiety (perhaps only real to an African), but the anxiety is not sustained and is soon replaced by a state of frenzy in which the patient is excited, noisy, incoherent, and perhaps filthy, aggressive,

and dangerously violent. The violence often results in homicide but is apt to be ill-directed and generalized ... Recovery usually occurs in a few hours or days and is as complete as it is rapid.... The subject subsequently always denies all memory for the period of the frenzy. The precipitating cause is usually clear, and most of the patients on recovery are themselves cognizant of at least some of the factors that produced their mental breakdown."

Psychiatric writers from many parts of Africa have referred, under a variety of other titles—"bouffée délirante," fear and guilt frenzy, periodic psychosis, pseudo-amok—to a syndrome which appears to be substantially the same. It has thus been referred to by Aubin[11] and Gallais and Planques[106] in the then French West Africa; Baudoux[16] in the Congo; Collomb[64] in Senegal; Dembovitz[82] in West African troops; Field[96, 97] in Ghana; Gelfand[111] in Rhodesia; Lambo[151] in Nigeria; Laubscher[155] in South Africa; Shelley and Watson[225] in Nyasaland; Smartt[233] in Tanzania; and Tewfik[243] in Uganda.

The most thorough study of "bouffées délirantes" in recent years has been made by Collomb[66]. Only a few salient points from this most valuable and comprehensive article can be recorded here. On the basis of an intensive study of 125 cases seen over a 14-month period in Senegal, he finds that this condition is extremely frequent— constituting about 30 per cent of all admissions to the mental hospital, and considers that it is the syndrome most characteristic of African psychiatry. It occurred most often in the 20–40-year age group; was rather more frequent among female admissions than among male; and affected all the local tribal groups, pagan or Mohammedan, about equally. It occurred, as a rule in persons without an antecedent psychiatric history. The onset was usually acute (77 per cent) and there was an associated organic or toxic condition in 25 per cent of his cases. He found that delusions were usually persecutory (72 per cent) and that visual hallucinations were nearly as frequent as verbal. He found that anxiety and confusion were only prominent in transplanted Africans and believed that these symptoms occur especially in transitional situations where a solution on indigenous lines is not quickly to be found. Most patients (90 per cent) made a full and rapid recovery, and the subsequent development of chronic or schizophrenic states was rare. He found that the development of this condition follows a pattern that is not seen as strange, either by the patient or his community, and that his family, far from rejecting him, will attempt his re-integration into the community and are usually successful in this. He found no resemblance to the schizophrenic process; there is no withdrawal, and the patient may even be better integrated into his society afterwards than he was before.

The number of patients affected by this condition has varied considerably in reported series of psychiatric cases. The present writer[50] recorded 21 cases of "frenzied anxiety" among 558 admissions in Kenya. Field[97] diagnosed 26 cases of "fear and guilt psychosis" among 123 psychiatric cases seen at the shrines of Ghana. Lambo[151] relegated 180 admissions ($4\frac{1}{2}$ per cent) to his unclassified psychosis group but included in this figure his "excito-motor syndrome" as well as the "periodic psychosis" which seems to correspond to "frenzied anxiety"; he found both these syndromes were much more prevalent in rural areas, together constituting over 11 per cent of all the rural psychiatric cases treated at Aro Hospital; and of the "periodic psychosis" he wrote that "it seems to be predominantly, if not wholly, confined to the primitive African and is more frequent in rural and primitive surroundings than in urban areas". Smartt[233] included 34 admissions (13·5 per cent) as unclassified psychoses and diagnosed 19 of these as suffering from "frenzied anxiety". Tewfik[243] relegated no less than 247 out of 304 admissions to an unclassified group of which he said: "the symptoms of patients in undiagnosed groups were fairly uniform ... sudden onset of confusion, persecutory delusions, vivid hallucinations and rapidly changing clinical picture." He also wrote: "In the more educated African this syndrome of restlessness, violence and hallucinations is much modified or often absent. It appears, therefore, that the rural African, whenever his sanity is threatened, responds in a stereotyped, dramatic way" and he considered in general that this was a non-specific frenzy which complicated the onset of all other psychoses.

Most writers record that the subjects recover quite quickly and completely, though some develop hysterical, somatic or Ganser syndromes before complete recovery. Field,[97] on the other hand, found that many of her "fear and guilt psychoses" occurred in latent schizophrenics, and that many of the subjects who appeared to recover quickly from the acute syndrome slipped quietly months later into schizophrenia, or had even been insane before.

Among her 26 cases, she observed that 9, either became schizophrenic later, or had been so before, or showed schizophrenic traits
at the time of the illness.

Taking all these findings into account, the present writer
believes that his earlier assessment[52] of the place occupied by this
syndrome in African psychiatry was a fair one. He wrote:

"These states occur on many backgrounds—of physical disease,
underlying psychosis or neurosis, or even of apparent normality—
and are precipitated by a variety of physical and mental traumata. It
may be surmised that physical or psychotic factors play a larger part
in the more lasting cases, and emotional factors a larger in the
transient. Anxiety, with or without depression, precedes the onset
of acute cases but is not sustained for long. It is always related by the
patient to bewitchment, and he is often fully cognizant of the
latter's origin and object. . . . Bewitchment often takes the place in
African life that conscience does in other cultures. The present
writer has often been aware in frenzied cases (and in others) that the
fear of sorcery was based far less on evidence of its occurrence than
on an unadmitted knowledge in the patient of wrongs done by
himself."

Collomb sees this syndrome as one that affects the personality
superficially and without disturbance of its deeper levels; as one
which enables people who develop mentally as members of a
group rather than on individual lines to act out and solve their
conflicts exteriorly; and as one which is well recognized and
quickly treated within the indigenous milieu, but which tends to
become more severe and prolonged in the transitional world.

The present writer finds this assessment entirely acceptable,
and would finally emphasize that the occurrence of this condition, which is rarely seen in the Western world, yet which is
surely common throughout Africa south of the Sahara, constitutes in itself a powerful argument—if one is still needed— for
dealing with Africans of this vast area as a whole, both in regard
to their psychiatry and their psychology.

Psychiatry of the American Negro

This subject can only be discussed quite briefly in this volume.

From a statistical point of view, Malzberg's[168] analysis of first admissions to the mental hospitals of the State of New York over a 3-year period remains the classic work. It appeared from this that there was a total average annual admission rate of 150·6 per 100,000 for the Negro population and of 73·7 for the White and that, when the rates were standardized for age, they became 224·7 and 97·4 respectively, with a ratio of 2·3 to 1·0. Important contrasts in the standardized rates as between the Whites and Negroes were observed in regard to general paralysis (with a Negro rate 4·1 times higher than the White); alcoholic psychoses (3·4 times higher); cerebral arteriosclerosis (2·9 times higher); senile psychoses (1·9 times higher); dementia praecox (2·0 times higher); and manic-depressive psychoses (1·5 times higher). When allowances are made for urbanization and migration—factors which are known to be directly related to such rates—the disparities diminish. In his final summary Malzberg says:

"We have shown that fundamental qualitative differences with respect to mental disease do not exist as between Negroes and Whites. There is not a type of mental disorder among Whites which is not to be found among Negroes. Contrariwise, Negroes suffer from no mental disorder that does not find its counterpart among Whites. It is clear, however, that there is a fundamental difference with respect to the incidence of mental disease, which is much more frequent among Negroes. To what is this difference due? Is it the result of some 'racial' qualities which make the Negro more susceptible to a mental and nervous breakdown? Of this there is no evidence . . . We turn therefore to a consideration of environmental factors and here we find ample explanation of the high rates of mental disease among Negroes. These rates are due to the direct and indirect influences of conditions of life over which the Negro has as yet little control."

Other writers, such as Robins et al.,[221] have commented on the relative frequency among American Negroes of disorders in the antisocial field—sociopathic states, alcoholism, and drug addiction.

It is also of interest to record that Williams *et al.*,[262] made a thorough autopsy study of 408 arterial circles of Willis in Nigeria and, comparing their findings with similar studies made in Whites (5,033) in Minnesota, and Whites (101) and Negroes (94) in Alabama, found that the percentage of subjects with no atherosclerosis was much higher at each age level above 45 years in the Nigerians than either the Whites or the Negroes studied in America.

Myrdal[186] has shown that low suicide rates are the rule in American Negroes but, according to Prudhomme,[213] this is less true of urban than rural Negroes, and Hendin[123] finds that suicide is twice as common among young Negro men of New York as among White men of the same age group.

Finally, Bromberg and Simon[44] have described under the title of the "Protest Psychosis" a condition which occurs reactively and commonly in American Negroes who are being held on a criminal charge or are convicted of one. It occurs in men who are rarely older than 35 years and who may or may not have had a previous history of mental illness. Apart from a variety of symptoms which bear a superficial resemblance to schizophrenic ones, it is characterized by delusions expressive of antagonism to White cultural values and by hallucinations, auditory or visual, which seems to conjure up imaginary "African" environments to replace the current environment of jail or hospital. The condition lasts from weeks to months and the writers find that it is usually misdiagnosed as schizophrenic. They see it, however, as a type of reactive psychosis and as a reflection of the widespread spirit of nationalism among non-Whites; and it seems to the present writer that, in this psychosis, reactive to an anxiety-laden situation—and in which the delusional and hallucinatory content conforms to the prevailing cultural or sub-cultural expectation— there is a close parallel to the "bouffées délirantes" so commonly seen in Africa. This parallel would seem in its turn to imply some basic psychological similarity between certain sections of the Negro populations both in Africa and America.

PART FIVE

PERSPECTIVES

Discussion

An attempt will now be made to put the data assembled in the earlier chapters into some perspective. Physical aspects will be considered in the first instance.

Whether or not the modern Negro derives partly from Caucasoid stock at the end of Pleistocene, as Coon[74] suggests, it is fairly clear that much of his ancestry diverged from the ancestors of the Caucasoids much earlier than that (perhaps about 35,000 years ago) and that at a time when, with the final passing of the Ice Age, the Caucasoids were moving up into Europe, his ancestors had moved, or were moving, into the sub-Saharan region of West Africa. There, it cannot be doubted, some adaptation to a tropical climate was developed. At least part of this adaptation was physical.

Until the end of the Pleistocene men were "food-gatherers" and lived in sparsely scattered groups, hunting over large tracts of land. Thereafter, about 10,000 years ago, agriculture and, later, pastoralism developed. These were great advances, which increased and stabilized the food supplies, and enabled many to live who would otherwise have died or never been born. But they carried dangers of their own; they pinned man far more closely to areas of land, and enabled populations to increase to the point where problems of survival shifted—from the dangers of attack by animal predators and starvation—to the battle with infection.

Variety of parasitism is most likely to occur in hosts whose population is both large and concentrated, and this is especially true where the parasite's life-history is complex. Where, for instance, the parasite depends for its survival on transmission from water snails to men and back again, its success is much dependent on the commonness of both its hosts. Stabilization of populations in limited areas of land also assists this process, as is well seen in those infections that depend on fly transmission from excreta. It may therefore be surmised that, in the early days of agriculture, one after another of the plagues that afflict mankind took advantage of this ideal situation and a heavy toll in human life.

With the passage of time, however, the parasite-host relationships evolved. Mackey's[163] contribution on this theme, in Africa, is a most illuminating one, and the rest of this paragraph is mainly inspired by this writer. As Mackey points out, it is by no means of advantage to most parasites for the host to die or even to develop morbid symptoms, and of still less advantage to the host. Although man's evolution is relatively slow, the evolution of a parasite species is apt to be as rapid as its members' lives are brief. And so commensalism arises, chiefly by evolution in the parasite, but also by evolution in the host. Mackey considers that, by a selective process, man in Africa has developed a greater capacity for hypertrophy of the reticulo-endothelial system and for an insensitivity to certain parasitic antigens, and that these capacities are therefore now ingrained in his genetic constitution. He considers that certain parasites (especially some species of *Plasmodium*, *Necator*, *Schistosoma*, and *Ascaris*) have achieved a degree of commensalism in East Africans which is not seen in Europeans, and that these parasites are now pathogenic in the former only when malnutrition complicates the picture. Certain other African parasites (such as *Trypanosoma* and *Onchocerca*) have not yet achieved commensalism in man because their invasion of the human host is only recent. Mackey infers that, where the commensalism has been successful, the main stages of the process must have occurred in earlier times when protein lack was not a problem. Finally, he believes that the various peculiar pathological states in Africans that Davies[78] attributes to an oestrinization basically malnutritional are based on genetic differences, and that "the hormonal make-up of the East African is genetic and has been brought about, at least to some extent, by a process of selective survival in hyper-endemic parasitic areas of those best able to tolerate their parasitic infections."

It is not to be believed, however, that all infections known to us impinged on man at once; and it may be surmised that, at any one time, there was usually one major scourge, and that, the other present-day human parasites had either reached commensalism or not yet arrived upon the human scene. Moreover, in 10,000 years it is likely that in many times and places there were periods of relative freedom from any serious infection in which, this check on human increase being lacking, the only limiting factor was the food supply. (That the population was kept in check receives support from Pearl's[200] conclusion that its number increased only very gradually and with minor fluctuations until about 300 years ago, since which time it has increased 5 times.)

Trowell and Davies[249] draw attention to the fact that kwashiorkor, or something very like it, has been described in many tropical and sub-tropical lands in Asia and America (as well as Africa) and has even been observed in the children of certain European towns. It is likely, after all, that agricultural living and the increase of population which accrues from this will tend to give rise to a protein-calorie imbalance, since wild game rapidly disappears from arable land and, where some pastoralism is practised, its products have seldom been efficiently exploited. It is therefore probable that we have latterly been witnessing a severe selective stage in the nutritional life of Africa, and that those children who survived were often those who were better adapted to a relative lack of high-class protein. Evolutionary processes are as likely to apply to nutritional factors as to others and it would seem as legitimate to apply Mackey's argument to malnutrition as to apply it to infection, and to believe that the African genetic "hormonal make-up" is also partly based on a process of selective survival in malnutritional areas which is likely to have been different from that in Europeans.

Indeed, in a recent article by Biss and 4 others[33] on the subject of serum cholesterol in the Masai—a purely pastoral tribe with a high protein diet—the investigators found a much greater ability to suppress cholesterol synthesis than is found in Whites, and regarded this ability as genetically determined. Although the Masai's diet is very different from that of most African peoples, these findings certainly support the general argument.

On the basis of this argument, one might expect that morbid conditions—which accrue in other countries from excess of certain food factors—would occur in Africans, adapted to a relative deficiency of such factors, with greater frequency or severity than occurs in the peoples of those countries, when the former are introduced to the diet of the latter. If cerebral atheroscherosis is partly related to such factors, Malzberg's[168] finding, in his survey of the predominantly urban population of New York State, that cerebral arteriosclerosis is nearly 3 times as common in Negroes as it is in Whites, would seem to support this expectation.

Climatic, infective, and nutritional factors are thus all likely to have played their part in moulding, on distinct lines, the genetic basis of the physical constitution of man in Africa.

*   *   *

Living in groups, however, gives rise to problems in the mental as well as the physical field and this becomes especially true when the groups increase in size, as followed the coming of agriculture. Man, like many other animals, has developed a social way of living. Though superior in intellectual power, he is physically weak, and his strength lies in his numbers provided he can live in bands. This development, though found in many other animals, is dependent in them on structural diversity within the species—as with ants—or on ingrained behaviour patterns which control aggression within the species—as with dogs and jackdaws. Where all are structurally and instinctively similar—as obtains in man—the experiment of social living is a dangerous one. Each individual develops on very similar lines with drives to sex, aggression, and acquisition whose free expression is not compatible with social life. These drives are never far below the surface and must be stamped on from an early age if societies are to survive.

It needs to be said here that many of the cultural features described in this book are not uniquely African. Thus the peoples studied by Malinowski,[167] Porteus,[205] and others, have developed something similar. Though varying much in detail, most non-literate groups insist on the observance of meticulous social rules and stamp effectively on independent thought and personal initiative. It is surely true that early Europeans experienced such restraints and, even in the Europe of today, their relics are not hard to find. It seems, therefore, that cultural patterns of this type are frequent, if not constant, concomitants of a certain stage in human social evolution.

It was observed before that chronic infections (whose effects are often partly malnutritional), and malnutrition itself, can act to diminish self-control and to increase egotism. Yet infections and malnutrition, either together or separately, have probably been very regularly associated with African rural life. Humid heat may act in the same way; it certainly seems to do so in Europeans. It may be, therefore, that the rigid control of the individual, of his thinking and behaviour, has often been doubly necessary at this stage of his development, and that it is only when man is freed from these afflictions that he becomes capable of profiting from a loosening of the cultural bonds.

Thus, in general, it would seem that the non-literate cultural modes may need *less* explaining than do later cultural modes.

* * *

As the present writer has attempted to show in an earlier chapter, most of the differences between the psychology of Africans and that of Europeans can be seen as the outcome of literacy in the latter or, in McLuhan's[176] language, of the substitution of an "eye" for an "ear" culture. For, it was surely this that paved the way for freedom of thought, personal initiative, and responsibility for one's behaviour on the basis of a few general principles.

One is therefore led to ask why, until lately, this great African population remained non-literate.

It is true that the written word has probably only been invented a few times in this world's history. Yet in other large agricultural populations its impact has been vital for many centuries. It is sometimes argued that its absence from sub-Saharan Africa is to be accounted for by the gross isolation of this country from outside influences in historic times. Yet it *has* been introduced, in its Arabic form, both through the Sudan and from the east coast, frequently enough. It has even been invented, on two occasions in the 19th century, by gifted individuals in Sierra Leone and the Cameroons (Biesheuvel).[23] Yet it failed to implant itself and grow, and this is the more surprising in view of the high level of organization and stability achieved by several West African kingdoms in other respects. Nor can this failure be attributed to the disruption of organized life in Africa by the Atlantic slave trade since Arabic literacy in the western Sudan goes back at least 850 years, according to Davidson,[75] or about 450 years before the beginning of that trade.

Viewing all these matters broadly therefore it seems to the

present writer that, apart from a temperament which may well
be constitutionally different, there remain 4 phenomena which
are hardly to be explained on purely environmental lines:

(1) The failure of the written word to spread in Africa till
    lately.
(2) The distinctive psycho-motor and EEG development of
    the African infant.
(3) The relatively poor achievement of American Negroes in
    psychological tests (particularly in logical analysis, abstract
    reasoning, and spatial conceptualization).
(4) The relative difficulty in dealing with 3-dimensional
    problems experienced by Africans.

Attempts to explain these remaining problems can only be
speculative but, in the first instance, one has to ask how far
American Negroes, particularly of North America (since this is
where they have been so thoroughly tested), are to be
regarded as representative of the sub-Saharan population of
Africa.

Aside from later miscegenation in America, which has been
discussed already, the ancestors of American Negroes were for
the most part Negroes of the Guinea Coast and its hinterland,
while a lesser but still considerable proportion were Bantu
Negroes from the Congo and Angola. In that sense therefore
they are fairly representative.

But what selection was effected by the slave trade? It has
been argued, quite tentatively, by Eysenck[90] that by reason of
only duller Negroes being taken and sold by their chiefs, or
by reason of more intelligent slaves in America escaping or
being destroyed as trouble-makers, "It is not impossible that
American Negroes may be the descendants of a highly selected
sample of African Negroes less bright than the total group". It
has also been argued, in an opposite sense, by Ransford[215] that
"the slavers victims were the youngest and healthiest numbers
of the community, and that the trade deprived the continent
of its most valuable genes".

In pursuit of the answer, something must be said about the
circumstances of the slave trade. This will be done as briefly as
possible, and for most of the details the present writer is
indebted to Ransford.[215]

The majority of the slaves were captured in expeditions by

great or petty African "kings" and their armed retainers; whole villages (either of their own people or of neighbouring groups) were surrounded and burned, and all the inhabitants either massacred or enslaved. The captives were marched off to the coast, perhaps hundreds of miles away, in a journey so arduous that anything up to half their numbers were expected to die. They were then held in fortified enclosures until sold to the ships' captains, or killed if unsaleable by reason of decrepitude or illness. The Atlantic voyage rarely took less than three months, and in such appalling conditions of over-crowding and insanitation that the loss of life was sometimes up to a third of those who embarked. The survivors were sold in the slave markets of the New World and many of these were sent to plantations where (in the Caribbean at least) about one-third commonly died within a year of arrival.

In the course of 4 centuries, probably at least 14,000,000 Negroes were transported to the New World and at least the same number were killed in the slavers' wars, or died on their trek to the coast, or on the Atlantic passage. Thus, by death or enslavement, perhaps about 75,000 people a year were lost to Africa over a period of 400 years. The latest years were the worst and by 1820 it was estimated that a Negro born in Guinea had 1 chance in 4 of being killed or enslaved in this trade.

To revert to the problem of the sort of selection that may have occurred, it would seem that this must be considered from two points of view—that of Africa, and that of America.

In regard to the African side of the picture; because of the great number of people involved (a number which must have largely depopulated many areas of the forest belt of West Africa) and because of the circumstances of their capture, there could hardly have been much selection at all. Apart from the fact that some of the chiefs, their families, and their warriors were exempt from enslavement and may have been of superior wit (which might account for the existence of a small intellectual élite to this day) the great bulk of the population is unlikely to show evidence of selection.

In regard to America, on the other hand, there must surely have been a considerable selection in favour of those with the strongest physique and the best will to live. But as far as intelligence is concerned, it is not at all clear that this was selected against. Insubordination and intelligence are not likely to correlate very highly together—Vicars of Bray are not rare and not stupid—and there must often have been a superior niche for intelligent slaves.

Thus, in sum, and as far as intellectual faculties are concerned, there would seem at present to be no justification for assuming any fundamental difference as between African and American Negroes.

*   *   *

To return therefore to the Old World and to the questions posed earlier, one might follow Biesheuvel[22] in this paragraph and postulate that from about 10,000 years ago when the Caucasoid peoples were populating western and northern Europe, these latter peoples were forced, by the exigencies of geography and climate, to produce better clothes, homes, ploughs, and sailing ships; to invent the mechanical devices that were needed for the making of these; and to abandon some of the rigidities of their old cultural modes. The African peoples, on the other hand, came or remained under the influence of a geography and climate which, though harsh in other ways, did not impede their ability to live without much alteration of their material techniques and without curtailment of their cultural modes.

These cultural modes may therefore have been given time to arrive at a level of perfection both for care and for control that was unique. Thus Leakey,[156] while recognizing the stagnation that overcame Africa, in recent millennia in other respects, has emphasized that in some ways Africans have advanced culturally further than Europeans—in family planning by spacing of childbirth, in avoiding the death penalty for murder, and in care for orphans, widows, and the aged.

One is therefore finally impelled to ask whether an "ear", as opposed to an "eye", culture has lasted for so long in Africa that an "ear psychology" has become ingrained in the mental constitution of its peoples. Biesheuvel[20], says "that at least in the auditory sphere, the African's ability to grasp, work out, remember, and create intricate new relations of a most abstract kind is by no means inferior to that displayed by the European in the visual or conceptual sphere".

As was mentioned in an earlier chapter, sounds are of much

greater significance to the hearer in indigenous African life than they are in modern urban life. This must have been particularly true of the sort of forest environment which was the homeland of the Negro, and where things and events are heard before they are seen. In this environment an alert attention to sounds and a facility for their swift interpretation must have had no small survival value. If these faculties have a genetic basis, they are therefore likely to have become a part of the African inheritance and, accordingly, are even likely to continue to govern an attitude to life in which the auditory aspect of the world of reality is regarded as its truest one.

To turn, therefore, once again to the four questions that were posed before, the present writer believes that this theory is relevant to all of them. For it would explain the long indifference in Africa to the written word; it would explain the lack of facility in all those mental activities that depend on a habit of visual (as opposed to auditory) synthesis and as observed in both African and American Negroes; and it may be relevant to the relative retardation of visual (as opposed to motor) development as observed in African infants in South Africa. It may also be relevant to the minor EEG differences between African and European adults recorded in Chapter 6 and to the "brain-fag syndrome" described in Chapter 9.

Advantage does not lie wholly with the European, even apart from the musical aspect. Mental integration on individual lines is essentially a conscious one, and depends on a cleavage between conscious and unconscious elements of the mind which is much less sharp in Africans. It depends on the denial, in adult conscious life, of desires and phantasies which are thus relegated to a world of darkness and of dreams, but which emerge, only too often, to determine patterns of thinking and behaviour which are incomprehensible or even incapacitating from the subject's conscious point of view. There is internal conflict, and a sacrifice of personal to social peace and happiness. There may be other sacrifices—of intuition, of human sympathy, of zest for life, of enjoyment of leisure.

These developments admittedly, are mostly the outcome of the post-Renaissance evolution of personality in Europe from one which, in Riesman's[219] terminology, is "tradition-directed" to one which is "inner-directed". As such, they are not racial. Nevertheless, in the present writer's view, this evolution was itself one outcome of the change in perceptual involvement which occurred about that time, and which has been a recurrent theme in the later chapters of this book.

Finally therefore one has to ask, on lines suggested by McLuhan's writings, whether an imbalance has occurred, and whether this recent evolution has, like the African one, become too exclusively dependent on one perceptual mode.

Bibliography

1   Aall, L. (1962) REVIEW AND NEWSLETTER, McGill Univ., 13, 54–7
2   Akinkugbe, O. O. (1969) E. AFR. MED. J., 46, 313–20
3   Akinkugbe, O. O. and Ojo, O. A. (1969) BRIT. MED. J. (Apr. 26), 222–4
4   Albino, R. C. and Thompson, V. J. (1956) BRIT. J. MED. PSYCHOL., 29, 177–210
5   Anastasi, A. and Foley, J. P. (1949) DIFFERENTIAL PSYCHOLOGY, N.Y.
6   Asuni, T. (1962) BRIT. MED. J. (Oct. 27), 1091–7
7   Asuni, T. (1966) SYMPOSIUM ON PSYCHIATRY IN AFRICA, Khartoum
8   Asuni, T. (1967) BRIT. J. PSY., 113, 1031–3
9   Asuni, T. (1970) TRANSCULT. PSYCHIAT. RESEARCH REVIEW, 7, 40–3
10 Asuni, T. and Pillutla, V. S. (1967) BRIT. J. PSYCHIAT., 113, 1375–9
11 Aubin, H. (1939) ANN. MÉD.—PSYCHOL., 97, 1–61
12 Basher, T. A. (1961) WORLD MENTAL HEALTH, 13, 1–5
13 Barbe, R. (1951) MÉD. TROP., 11, 33–8
14 Bateson, G. (1944) TRANS. N.Y. ACAD. SCI., 6, 137–41
15 Bateson, G. (1944) In: Hunt, J. McV. ed. PERSONALITY AND THE BEHAVIOUR DISORDERS, N.Y.
16 Baudoux, R. (1952) INST. ROYAL COLON. BELGE MÉMOIRES, 22, 1–39
17 Bean, R. B. (1906) AM.J. ANAT., 5, 353
18 Berman, S. (1958) REVIEW AND NEWSLETTER, McGill Univ., 4, 54–8
19 Bianchi, L. (1937) ARCH. ITAL. ANAT. EMBRIOL., 39, 1
20 Biesheuvel, S. (1943) AFRICAN INTELLIGENCE, Johannesburg
21 Biesheuvel, S. (1952) AFRICAN STUDIES, 11, 45–58, 105–17
22 Biesheuvel, S. (1956) THE LISTENER (Apr. 12), 385–6
23 Biesheuvel, S. (1956) THE LISTENER (May 10), 601
24 Biesheuvel, S. (1958) REVIEW AND NEWSLETTER, McGill Univ., 4, 42–9
25 Biesheuvel, S. (1958) CSA/CCTA PUBL. 35, Bukavu, 122–6
26 Biesheuvel, S. (1963) S. AFR. J. OF SCI., 59, 375–86
27 Biesheuvel, S. (1966) S. AFR. J. OF SCI., 62, 3–7
28 Biesheuvel, S. (1967) In: SYMPOSIUM ON DROUGHT AND DEVELOPMENT, Bulawayo. (May), 151–5
29 Billinghurst, J. R. (1966) E. AFR. MED. J., 43, 385–93
30 Billinghurst, J. R. (1970) E. AFR. MED. J., 47, 653–63
31 Billington, W. R. (1942) E. AFR. MED. J., 22, 4
32 Billington, W. R. (1966) E. AFR. MED. J., 43, 469–73
33 Biss, K., Ho, K. J., Mikkelson, N., Lewis, L., and Taylor, C. B. (1971) NEW ENGLAND J. MED., 284, 694
34 Blanchard, P. (1944) In: Hunt, J. McV., ed. PERSONALITY AND THE BEHAVIOUR DISORDERS, N.Y.
35 Bohannan, P. (1960) ed: AFRICAN HOMICIDE AND SUICIDE, Princeton, N.J.
36 Bork-Feltkamp, A. J. van (1939) ACTA NEERL. MORPH., 3, No.1
37 Boroffka, A. (1966) E. AFR. MED. J., 43, 378–84
38 Boroffka, A. and Marinho, A. A. (1961) In: Lambo, T. A. ed. FIRST PAN-AFRICAN PSYCHIAT. CONFERENCE, Ibadan, Nigeria, 195–7
39 Marinho, A. A. (1963) REVIEW AND NEWSLETTER, McGill Univ., 15, 44–6
40 Bourdel, L. (1949) REVUE. MENS. COM. NAT. ORG. FRANC., 23, 9
41 Bowlby, J. (1952) MATERNAL CARE AND MENTAL HEALTH, (WHO Monograph No.2) Geneva
42 Brelsford, W. V. (1950) AFRICA, 20, 46–54
43 Brock, J. F. and Autret, M. (1952) KWASHIORKOR IN AFRICA, (WHO Monograph, No.8) Geneva
44 Bromberg, W. and Simon, F. (1968) ARCH. GEN. PSYCHIAT., 19, 155–60

45   Brown, A. (1961) In: Lambo, T. A., ed. FIRST PAN-AFRICAN PSYCHIATRIC CONFER-
     ENCE, Ibadan, Nigeria, 134–8

46   Brown, R. C. (1938) REPORT III ON THE CARE AND TREATMENT OF LUNATICS IN THE
     BRITISH WEST AFRICAN COLONIES, Nigeria

47   Brown, R. E. (1965) E. AFR. MED. J., 42, 584–95

48   Carman, J. A. and Roberts M. A. W. (1934) E. AFR. MED. J., 11, 107–24

49   Carothers, J. C. (1945) E. AFR. MED. J., 22, 4–6

50   Carothers, J. C. (1947) J. MENT. SCI., 93, 548–97

51   Carothers, J. C. (1951) J. MENT. SCI., 97, 12–48

52   Carothers, J. C. (1953) THE AFRICAN MIND IN HEALTH AND DISEASE, (WHO mono-
     graph 17) Geneva

53   Carothers, J. C. (1954) THE PSYCHOLOGY OF MAU MAU, Govt. Printer, Nairobi

54   Carothers, J. C. (1959) PSYCHIATRY, 22, 307–20

55   Carstairs, G. M. (1958) LANCET , (June 7), 1217–20

56   CSA CCTA (1959) SYMPOSIUM ON BASIC PSYCHOLOGY OF AFRICAN AND MADAGASCAN
     POPULATIONS, Tananarive

57   Chauhan, P. S. (1968) E. AFR. MED. J., 45, 545–51

58   Cheneveau (1937) ANN. MÉD. PHARM. COLON., 35, 431

59   Clark, M. (1951) E. AFR. MED. J., 28, 229–36

60   Clausen, S. W. (1950) In: Jolliffe, N., Tisdall, F. F. and Cannon, P. R., CLINICAL
     NUTRITION, N.Y.

61   Cobb, W. M. (1934) J. NEGRO. EDUC., 3, 340

62   Cobb, W. M. (1942) AMER. J. PHYS. ANTHROP., 29, 113

63   Collis, W. R. F. (1961) In: Lambo, T. A. ed. FIRST PAN-AFRICAN PSYCHIATRIC
     CONFERENCE, Ibadan, Nigeria

64   Collomb, H. (1959) REVIEW AND NEWSLETTER, McGill Univ., 6, 34–6

65   Collomb, H. (1965) PSYCHOPATHOLOGIE AFRICAINE, 1, 11–84

66   Collomb, H. (1965) PSYCHOPATHOLOGIE AFRICAINE, 1, 167–239

67   Collomb, H. (1967) CANAD. PSYCHIAT. ASS. J., 12, 451–65

68   Collomb, H., Diop, M. and Ayats, H. (1962) CAHIERS D'ÉTUDES AFRICAINES, 2,
     139–44

69   Collomb, H. and Massat, R. (1962) FACULTÉ MIXTE MÉD. PHARM. DE .DAKAR,
     6–32

70   Collomb, H. and Zwingelstein, J. (1961) In: Lambo, T. A. ed. FIRST PAN-AFRICAN
     PSYCHIATRIC CONFERENCE, Ibadan, 227–34

71   Collomb, H. and Picca, M (1962) FACULTÉ MIXTE MÉD. PHARM. DE DAKAR, 47–58

72   Connolly, C. J. (1950) EXTERNAL MORPHOLOGY OF THE PRIMATE BRAIN, Springfield,
     Ill.

73   Coon, C. S. (1962) THE ORIGIN OF RACES, N.Y.

74   Coon, C. S. (1965) THE LIVING RACES OF MAN, London

75   Davidson, B. (1964) THE AFRICAN PAST, London

76   Davie, M. R. (1949) NEGROES IN AMERICAN SOCIETY, N.Y.

77   Davies, J. N. P. (1949) BRIT. MED. J, 2, 676

78   Davies, J. N. P. (1952) ANNU. REV. MED., 3, 99

79   Dayton, N. A. (1940) NEW FACTS ON MENTAL DISORDER, N.Y

80   Dean, R. F. A. (1960) E. AFR. MED. J., 37, 378–83

81   Dean, R. F. A. and Burgess, H. J. L. (1962) E. AFR. MED. J., 39, 411–16

82   Dembovitz, N. (1945) J. OF R.A.M.C., 84, 70

83   Donnison, C. P. (1929) LANCET, 1, 6

84   Dougall, J. W. C. (1932) AFRICA, 5, 249

85   Dunn, L. C. (1951) RACE AND BIOLOGY, UNESCO, Paris

86   East, W. N. (1936) MEDICAL ASPECTS OF CRIME, London

87   Edozien, J. C. (1961) In: Lambo, T. A. ed. FIRST PAN-AFRICAN PSYCHIATRIC
     CONFERENCE, Ibadan, Nigeria

88 Ellenberger, H. (1960) AM. J. PSYCHOTHERAPY, 14, 158–73
89 Eysenck, H. G. (1964) ENCOUNTER, (June), 53
90 Eysenck, H. G. (1971) RACE, INTELLIGENCE AND EDUCATION, London
91 Faladé, S. -A. (1960) LE CONCOURS MÉD. (Feb.), 1005
92 Faris, R. E. L. (1944) In: Hunt, J. McV., ed. PERSONALITY AND THE BEHAVIOUR DISORDERS, N.Y.
93 Ferguson, J. C., Mackay, N. and Watson, W. C. (1968) E. AFR. MED. J., 45, 663
94 Fick, M. L. (1929) S. AFR. J. SCI., 26, 904–20
95 Fick, M. L. (1939) THE EDUCABILITY OF THE SOUTH AFRICAN NATIVE, Johannesburg
96 Field, M. J. (1958) J. MENT. SCI., 104, 1043–51
97 Field, M. J. (1960) SEARCH FOR SECURITY, London
98 Forde, D. and Jones, G. I. (1950) ETHNOGRAPHIC SURVEY OF AFRICA, WESTERN AFRICA, PART III, London
99 Forster, E. F. B. (1958) CSA/CCTA PUBLICATION, 35, 37–41
100 Fortes, M. and Mayer, D. Y. (1966) CAHIER D'ÉTUDES AFRICAINES, 6, 5–40
101 Foster, R. M. and Harries, J. R. (1970) E. AFR. MED. J., 47, 693–4
102 Fraser B. N. (1959) BRIT. MED. J. (March 21), 761–4
103 Gallais, P. and Charlopain, L. (1951) MÉD. TROP., 11, 62
104 Gallais, P., Corriol, J. and Bert, J. (1949) MÉD. TROP., 9, 693
105 Gallais, P., Miletto, G., Corriol, J. and Bert, J. (1951) MÉD. TROP., 11, 128–46
106 Gallais, P. and Planques, L. (1951) MÉD. TROP., 11, 5–32
107 Garnham, P. C. C. (1968) E. AFR. MED. J., 45, 641–50
108 Gates, R. R. (1958) AGMG, 9, 165–84
109 Geber, M. and Dean, R. F. A. (1957) LANCET, (June 15), 1216–9
110 Geber, M. and Dean, R. F. A. (1964) BOURRIER, 14, 425–37
111 Gelfand, M. (1947) THE SICK AFRICAN, 2nd ed., Cape Town
112 Gelfand, M. (1948) E. AFR. MED. J., 25, 110–12
113 Gelfand, M. (1961) MEDICINE IN TROPICAL AFRICA, London
114 Gesell, A. and Ilg, F. L. (1943) INFANT AND CHILD IN THE CULTURE OF TODAY, N.Y.
115 Gillis, L. (1951) In: Lambo, T. A. ed. FIRST PAN-AFRICAN PSYCHIATRIC CONFERENCE, Ibadan, 236–8
116 Gini, C. (1960) THE MANKIND QUARTERLY, I, 120–5
117 Gluckman, M. (1954) THE MAU MAU RITUALS, *Manchester Guardian* (March 19)
118 Gordon, H. L. (1934) EUGEN. REV., 25, 223
119 Gordon, H. L. (1936) E. AFR. MED. L., 12, 327–35
120 Gorer, G. (1935) AFRICA DANCES; A BOOK ABOUT WEST AFRICAN NEGROES, London
121 Great Britain Committee on Nutrition in the colonial Empire (1939) NUTRITION IN THE COLONIAL EMPIRE, London
122 Handlin, O. (1963) THE AMERICAN PEOPLE, London
123 Hendin, H. (1969) ARCH. GEN. PSYCHIAT., 21, 407–22
124 Herskovitz, M. J. (1930) AFRICA, 3, 59–77
125 Herskovitz, M. J. (1955) CULTURAL ANTHROPOLOGY, N.Y.
126 Hofmeyr, J. D. J. (1967) In: Kuttner, R. E. ed. RACE AND MODERN SCIENCE, N.Y.
127 Howells, W. (1967) MANKIND IN THE MAKING, Harmondsworth
128 Hughes, C. C. (1961) In: Lambo, T. A. ed. FIRST PAN-AFRICAN PSYCHIATRIC CONFERENCE, Ibadan, 143–6
129 Hunter, M. (1939) A STUDY OF THE RORSCHACH 'ERLEBNIS-TYPUS' OF COMPARABLE WHITE AND NEGRO SUBJECTS, N.Y.
130 Huntington, E. (1951) PRINCIPLES OF HUMAN GEOGRAPHY, 6th ed. London
131 Hutt, M. S. R. and Coles, R. (1969) E. AFR. MED. J., 46, 342–58
132 Hutton, P. W. (1956) E. AFR. MED. J., 33, 209–23
133 Huxley, J. (1942) EVOLUTION, THE MODERN SYNTHESIS, London
134 Jacobs, M. and Stern, B. J. (1947) OUTLINE OF ANTHROPOLOGY, Cambridge
135 Jakovljevic, V. (1964) TRANSCULT. PSYCHIAT. RESEARCH REV., I, 55–8

136 Jarvis, G. A. (1953) QUARTERLY REVIEW PAEDIAT. (Aug. 8)
137 Jelliffe, D. B. (1952) TRANS. R. SOC. TROP. MED. HYG., 13, 46
138 Jeffreys, M. J. W. (1951) AFR. STUD., 10, 1–40
139 Jilek, W. G. and Jilek-Aall, L. M. (1970) TRANSCULT. PSYCHIAT. RESEARCH REV., 7, 43–8
140 Kagwa, B. H. (1964) E. AFR. MED. J., 560–61
141 Kaushik, S. C. (1961) In: Lambo, T. A. ed. FIRST PAN-AFRICAN PSYCHIATRIC CONFERENCE, Ibadan
142 Kendrew, W. G. (1961) THE CLIMATES OF THE CONTINENTS, 5th ed.   London
143 Kenyatta, J. (1938) FACING MOUNT KENYA, London
144 Keys, A. et al (1963) CIRCULATION, 28, 381
145 Keys, A., Brozek, J., Henschel, Mockelsen, O. and Taylor, H. L. (1950) THE BIOLOGY OF HUMAN STARVATION, Minneapolis
146 Kidd, D. (1906) SAVAGE CHILDHOOD, London
147 Klineberg, O. (1950) INT. SOC. SCI. BULL., 2, 3
148 Krapf, E. E. (1959) MED. HYG., 17, 123
149 Lambo, T. A. (1955) J. MENT. SCI., 101, 239–66
150 Lambo, T. A. (1956) BRIT. MED. J., 2, 1388
151 Lambo, T. A. (1960) BRIT. MED. J. (Dec. 10), 1696–1704
152 Lambo, T. A. (1960) W. AFR. MED. J., 9, 95–104
153 Lambo, T. A. (1961) In: Lambo, T. A., ed. FIRST PAN-AFRICAN PSYCHIATRIC CONFERENCE, Ibadan
154 Lamont, A. McE. and Blignault, W. J. (1953) S. AFR. MED. J., 27, 637–9
155 Laubscher, B. J. F. (1937) SEX, CUSTOM AND PSYCHOPATHOLOGY, London
156 Leakey, L. S. B. (1961) THE PROGRESS AND EVOLUTION OF MAN IN AFRICA, London
157 Leather, C. M. and Leather, H. M. (1957) E. AFR. MED. J., 34, 589–92
158 Leighton, A. H. and Hughes, J. M. (1961) In: Lambo, T. A. ed. FIRST PAN-AFRICAN PSYCHIATRIC CONFERENCE, Ibadan, 138–41
159 Leighton, A. H., Lambo, T. A., Hughes, C. C., Leighton, D. C., Murphy, J. M. and Macklin, D. B. (1963) PSYCHIATRIC DISORDER AMONG THE YORUBA, N.Y.
160 Leighton, D. C. (1961) In: Lambo, T. A. ed. FIRST PAN-AFRICAN PSYCHIATRIC CONFERENCE, Ibadan, 141–3
161 Lewis, J. H. (1942) THE BIOLOGY OF THE NEGRO, Chicago
162 Luder, J. and Musoke, L. K. (1955) LANCET (March), 622
163 Mackey, J. P. (1953) E. AFR. MED. J., 30, 13–41
164 Mahmood, A. (1968) E. AFR. MED. J., 45, 720–5
165 Mairlot, F. (1958) CSA/CCTA PUBLICATION 35, Bukavu, 31–4
166 Maistriaux, R. (1955) REVUE DES PSYCHOL. DES PEUPLES, 10, 167–91
167 Malinowski, B. (1929) THE SEXUAL LIFE OF SAVAGES IN NORTH-WESTERN MELANESIA, London
168 Malzberg, B. (1944) In: Klineberg, O. ed. CHARACTERISTICS OF THE AMERICAN NEGRO, N.Y.
169 Malzberg, B. (1950) AM. J. MENT. DEF., 54, 266–81
170 Margetts, E. L. (1958) MED. PROC., 4, 679–83
171 Margetts, E. L. (1959) E. AFR. MED. J., 36, 257–63
172 Margetts, E. L. (1960) E. AFR. MED. J., 37, 32–6
173 Margetts, E. L. (1967) ECONOMIC BOTANY, 21, 358–62
174 Marwick, M. (1956) THE LISTENER, (Apr. 26), 490–2
175 McGurk, F. C. J. (1967) In: Kuttner R. E. ed. RACE AND MODERN SCIENCE, N.Y.
176 McLuhan, M. (1962) THE GUTENBURG GALAXY, London
177 Mead, M. (1947) AM. J. ORTHOPSYCHIAT., 17, 633
178 Mead, M. (1947) PSYCHIATRY, 10, 57
179 Merrill, G. G. and Cook, E. E. (1957) EEG CLIN. NEUROPHYSIOL., 9, 531–2
180 Moffson, A. (1955) S. AFR. MED. J., 29, 689–92

181 Monekosso, G. L. (1961) In: Lambo, T. A., ed. FIRST PAN-AFRICAN PSYCHIATRIC CONFERENCE, Ibadan

182 Monekosso, G. L. (1966) E. AFR. MED. J., 43, 353

183 Muller, H. J. (1952) In: THE RACE CONCEPT: RESULTS OF AN INQUIRY, UNESCO

184 Mundy-Castle, A. C., McKiever, B. L. and Prinslov, T. (1953) A COMPARATIVE STUDY OF THE EEGS OF NORMAL AFRICANS AND EUROPEANS OF SOUTHERN AFRICA, Johannesburg

185 Muwazi, E. M. K. and Trowell, H. C. (1944) E. AFR. MED. J., 21, 2–20

186 Myrdal, G. (1944) AN AMERICAN DILEMMA; THE NEGRO PROBLEM AND MODERN DEMOCRACY, N.Y.

187 Odegard, O. (1951) In: Lambo, A. T. ed. FIRST PAN-AFRICAN PSYCHIATRIC CONFERENCE, Ibadan, 150–6

188 Odhalo, J. (1962) E. AFR. MED. J., 39, 694–701

189 Ojiambo, H. P. (1966) E. AFR. MED. J., 43, 366–77

190 Oliver, R. A. C. (1932) E. AFR. MED. J., 9, 160

191 Orley, J. (1969) TRANSCULT. PSYCHIAT. RESEARCH REV., 6, 162–6

192 Ortigues, M-C. and Ortigues, E. (1966) OEDIPE AFRICAIN, Paris

193 Osborne, R. T. (1967) In: Kuttner, R. E. ed. RACE AND MODERN SCIENCE, N.Y.

194 Osuntokun, B. O. (1969) E. AFR. MED. J., 46, 385–94

195 Pampiglione, G. (1965) BRIT. MED. J., (Sept. 4), 573–5

196 Parin, P., Morgenthaler, M. and Parin-Matthey, G. (1967) PSYCHOPATH. AFRICAINE, 3, 195–206

197 Parrinder, G. (1969) In: Legum, C. ed. AFRICA HANDBOOK, Harmondsworth

198 Parry, J. H. and Sherlock, P. M. (1960) A SHORT HISTORY OF THE WEST INDIES, London

199 Pearl, R. (1934) SCIENCE, 80, 431

200 Pearl, R. (1937) AMER. NAT., 71, 732

201 Pendle, G. (1963) A HISTORY OF LATIN AMERICA, London

202 Penrose, L. S. (1949) THE BIOLOGY OF MENTAL DEFECT, London

203 Piaget, J. (1930) THE CHILD'S CONCEPTION OF PHYSICAL CAUSALITY, London

204 Piraux, A. (1961) In: Lambo, T. A. ed. FIRST PAN-AFRICAN PSYCHIATRIC CONFERENCE, Ibadan, 95–9

205 Porteus, S. D. (1937) PRIMITIVE INTELLIGENCE AND ENVIRONMENT, N.Y.

206 Price, A. C. (1962) GENETIC PSYCHOLOGY MONOGRAPHS 65, Univ. of Florida, 3–52

207 Prince, R. H. (1960) CANAD. PSYCHIAT. ASS. J., 5, 65

208 Prince, R. H. (1960) J. MENT. SCI., 106, 559–70

209 Prince, R. H. (1960) REVIEW AND NEWSLETTER, McGill Univ., 7, 31–3

210 Prince, R. H. (1961) In: Lambo, T. A. ed. FIRST PAN-AFRICAN PSYCHIATRIC CONFERENCE, Ibadan, 279–88

211 Prince, R. H. (1962) REVIEW AND NEWSLETTER, McGill Univ., 13, 42–50

212 Prince, R. H. (1968) CANAD. J. OF AFR. STUDIES, I, 177–92

213 Prudhomme, C. (1938) PSYCHOANAL. REV., 25, 372

214 Raman, A. C. (1960) WORLD MENTAL HEALTH, 12, 152–62

215 Ransford, O. (1971) THE SLAVE TRADE, London

216 Rapaport, D. (1951) In: Josiah Macey Jr. Foundation, PROBLEMS OF CONSCIOUSNESS, TRANSACTION OF THE 2ND CONFERENCE, (March), N.Y.

217 Raum, O. F. (1940) CHAGA CHILDHOOD, London

218 Ribble, M. A. (1944) In: Hunt, J. McV. ed. PERSONALITY AND THE BEHAVIOUR DISORDERS, N.Y.

219 Riesman, D. (1950) THE LONELY CROWD, Yale Univ.

220 Ritchie, J. F. (1943) THE AFRICAN AS SUCKLING AND AS ADULT, London

221 Robins, L. N., Murphy, G. E., Woodruff, R. A. and King, L. J. (1971) ARCH. GEN. PSYCHIAT., 24, 338–45

222 Savage, C. and Prince, R. (1963) REVIEW AND NEWSLETTER, McGill Univ., 15, 44–6
223 Shaper, A. G. (1969) E. AFR. MED. J., 46, 228–45
224 Shaper, A. G., Wright, G. H. and Kyobe, J. (1969) E. AFR. MED. J., 46, 273–81
225 Shelley, H. M. and Watson, W. H. (1936) J. MENT. SCI., 82, 1–30
226 Sherman, H. C. and Lanford, C. S. (1951) ESSENTIALS OF NUTRITION, 3rd ed. N.Y.
227 Shuey, A. M. (1966) THE TESTING OF NEGRO INTELLIGENCE, 2nd ed. N.Y.
228 Silvera, W. D. and Jelliffe, D. B. (1952) J. TROP. MED. HYG., 55, 73
229 Simmons, K. (1942) HUM. BIOL. 473
230 Simon, K. (1951) E. AFR. MED. J., 28, 75–9
231 Simons, H. J. (1958) J. MENT. SCI., 104, 377–88
232 Slater, E., Beard, A. W. and Glithero, E. (1963) BRIT. J. PSYCHIAT., 109, 95 –150
233 Smartt, C. G. F. (1956) J. MENT. SCI., 102, 441–66
234 Smartt, C. G. F. (1959) E. AFR. MED. J., 36, 91–8
235 Soskin, S. and Levine, R. (1950) In: Jolliffe, N., Tisdall, F. F., Cannon, P. R. CLINICAL NUTRITION, N.Y.
236 South African Commissioner for Mental Hygiene Annual Report 1960
237 Sow, D. (1962) THESIS PRESENTED AT THE UNIV. OF DAKAR
238 Stephen, E. and Robertson, J. (1965) In: Howells, J. G. ed. MODERN PERSPECTIVES IN CHILD PSYCHIATRY, London
239 Stephens, A. J. H. (1970) E. AFR. MED. J., 47, 383–8
240 Stoch, M. B. and Smythe, P. M. (1963) ARCH. DIS. CHILDH., 38, 546–52
241 Sullivan, H. S. (1953) THE INTERPERSONAL THERAPY OF PSYCHIATRY, N.Y.
242 Suttie, I. D. (1935) THE ORIGINS OF LOVE AND HATE, London
243 Tewfik, G. I. (1958) CSA/CCTA PUBLICATION 35, Bukavu, 127–38
244 Thouless, R. H. (1937) GENERAL AND SOCIAL PSYCHOLOGY, 2nd ed. London
245 Tooth, G. (1950) STUDIES IN MENTAL ILLNESS IN THE GOLD COAST, London
246 Tracey, H. (1954) AFRICAN AFFAIRS, 53, 234–41
247 Trowell, H. C. (1948) E. AFR. MED. J., 25, 236
248 Trowell, H. C. (1950) LANCET, 2, 454
249 Trowell, H. C. and Davies, J. N. P. (1952) BRIT. MED. J., 2, 796
250 Union of South Africa Mental Hospital Departmental Committees Report 1937, Pretoria
251 Verhaegen, P. (1955) ACTA NEUROL. PSYCHIAT. BELGICA, 55, 111–22
252 Verhaegen, P. (1956) ACTA NEUROL. PSYCHIAT. BELGICA, 56, 842–52
253 Vint, F. W. (1932) E. AFR. MED. J., 9, 30
254 Vint, F. W. (1934) J. ANAT., 68, 216–23
255 Vyncke, J. (1957) ACAD. R. DES SCIENCES COLON., Brussels
256 Vyncke, J. (1958) CSA/CCTA PUBLICATION 35, Bukavu, 52–5
257 Walker, E. A. (1957) A HISTORY OF SOUTHERN AFRICA, 3rd ed.
258 Warren, W. (1965) In: Howells, J. G. ed. MODERN PERSPECTIVES IN CHILD PSYCHIATRY, London
259 Westermann, D. (1939) THE AFRICAN TODAY AND TOMORROW, London
260 WHO, Third Report of the Expert Committee on Mental Health, Geneva, 1953
261 WHO, Eighth Report of the Expert Committee on Mental Health, Geneva, 1960
262 Williams, A. O., Resch, J. A. and Loewenson, R. B. (1971) E. AFR. MED. J., 48, 152–62
263 Williams, A. W. (1941) E. AFR. MED. J., 18, 109–17
264 Williams, C. D. (1938) LANCET, 1, 97
265 Wintrob, R. and Wittkower, R. D (1966) TRANSCULT. PSYCHIAT. RESEARCH REVIEW, 3, 149–52
266 Wittkower, E. D. and Fried, J. (1958) INT. J. OF SOCIAL PSYCH., 3, 245–52
267 Wittkower, E. D., Murphy, H. B. and Fried J. (1960) REVIEW AND NEWSLETTER, McGill Univ., 9, 2–17
268 Wright, F. J. (1941) E. AFR. MED. J., 18, 226–35

Index